S. S. GREAT EASTERN

The Greatest Iron Ship
S. S. GREAT EASTERN

George S. Emmerson

David & Charles
Newton Abbot   London   North Pomfret (Vt)

British Library Cataloguing in Publication Data

Emmerson, George Sinclair
  S.S. Great Eastern
  1. Great Eastern (*Ship*)
  I. Title
  387.2'43   VM383.G7

  ISBN 0–7153–8054–0

Typeset and printed in Great Britain by
Redwood Burn Limited Trowbridge and Esher
for David & Charles (Publishers) Limited
Brunel House Newton Abbot Devon

Published in the United States of America
by David & Charles Inc
North Pomfret Vermont 05053 USA

CONTENTS

ILLUSTRATIONS

ILLUSTRATIONS

1

THE CONCEPTION OF THE GREAT EASTERN

By the middle of the nineteenth century the people of Britain were not easily impressed; they thought they had seen everything. Steam engines sped them at frightening speeds over a tangled network of iron railways from one end of the country to the other; cheap manufactured goods poured from great steam-driven factories in fantastic variety, and so rapid was change that yesterday's glories were today's commonplaces. The Great Exhibition of 1851 had displayed the industrial achievements of the era and engineers could point to great iron bridges and powerful machines of a size unimaginable but a short time before. The 'last of the exclusive places' of the world were being opened up and, as one writer remarked, with the vastly increased speed of communications, and the skills of the printer and engraver, Hong Kong would soon be as familiar as the Isle of Dogs. 'What remains to be seen?' he asked, 'Where is a man to go for a new sensation or a novel sight?' In answer, he thought he could say: 'On either side of the River Thames, in the midst of those dreary regions known as East Greenwich and Millwall, where the atmosphere is tarry, and everything seems slimy and amphibious, where it is hard to say where the land has been rescued from the water or the water has encroached upon the land, two gigantic schemes are in progress 'which if not entire novelties, are at least as near approaches to it as this generation was ever likely to witness.'

These were an Atlantic submarine telegraph cable being spun and coiled like the snake of Scandinavian mythology which was said to encircle the world, and, on the other bank of the river at Millwall, a 'leviathan ship, the Great Eastern', the immense bulk of which, the writer continued, it was impossible for the mind to appreciate and realize at once; an immensity so great in comparison with all the notions previously conceived of monster ships, which seemed to elude comprehension and 'weigh upon the mind as a kind of iron nightmare'. But thirty years earlier the very idea of an iron ship of any size strained the comprehension of many, yet now, not only was the most recent Cunarder, the *Persia*, of iron and the largest ship afloat, but a prodigious monster, twice as long and broad as the *Persia* and upwards of six times the displacement, was being built broadside-on to the river with all seriousness. 'Look'ee here,' said an old salt to a gaping visitor, pointing his pipe with deliberation at the great hull on her cradles, 'here's her starn and here's her stem, and here's the water, and how they are going to launch her I can't figure noways.' Nor could thousands of others.

The launch was not the only challenge thrown down by the *Great Eastern* and picked up by the engineers, naval architects, shipbuilders and entrepreneurs associated with her. Her great size posed novel problems at every turn and if she was not *the* greatest engineering achievement of the century, she was one of the greatest and certainly the most sensational. It was strangely appropriate that the *Great Eastern* and Cyrus Field's first Atlantic telegraph cable were being constructed within sight of each other; fate was ultimately to bring them together in an historic union.

The *Great Eastern* epitomized the aspirations, self-confidence and entrepreneurial spirit of her time as did no other creation of the hand and mind of man, and the engineering skill of which she was a product, no less than her bizarre history, is of the greatest fascination to an age which no less than its predecessor thinks that it has seen everything. Her story has so many elements of grotesque fantasy, the natural prey of the journalist, that it is not surprising that no serious history of the great ship has been able to emerge.

In retrospect, we can see the *Great Eastern* as a premature anticipation of the great transatlantic passenger liners of the early twentieth century. She represented an immense step in proportions and complications from her greatest predecessors, and the strain she imposed upon the capacity of those who aspired to build and operate her, and upon the confidence of those who financed her, was commensurately great. But the gambling spirit was as prominent among English financiers of the period as it was among the gentlemen of the turf, and often they were one and the same. They played for high stakes and they were not encumbered by too much conscience in the matter. The railway mania was of recent memory and industrial speculation had made and destroyed many fortunes overnight. To

10

English capitalists one could address at this time more than any other the famous lines of Montrose:

> He either loves his fate too much,
> Or his desserts are small,
> Who will not put it to the touch
> To win or lose it all.

In the affairs of men, however, there are fascinating occasions when grandeur and the ridiculous are linked in grotesque partnership. It was the misfortune of the *Great Eastern*, grand and sublime in many ways, so often to illustrate this. There was, for instance, something of the absurd in the sight of a gigantic, outsize iron ship, over six times the displacement of the largest vessel afloat, being stuck on dry land, and obdurately resisting all efforts to move her into the water. It was embarrassing enough without all the world looking on. Yet our hearts and admiration go out to the stocky figure of Isambard Kingdom Brunel, dwarfed forlornly in his coarse working clothes by the immense iron cliffs and overhangs of the mammoth he had created, struggling with fate and enduring ridicule and a mortification to which he was peculiarly sensitive, but triumphing in the end. It is the very stuff of heroic myth and legend. But no matter how stupid and ridiculous some of it may seem, especially to condescending modern eyes, there was much reason in it, although it is difficult to deny that in the event it showed technology running ahead of commercial capacity in a way that has often happened in more recent times.

The *Great Eastern* was not built because someone simply wanted to build a monster ship. There were some very persuasive scientific and practical considerations which argued for such a ship, for a given duty on a given station. There was, too, in I.K. Brunel a bold and imaginative engineer for whom ambitious challenges held an irresistible fascination and inducement. The occasion found the man in a somewhat circuitous way, yet somehow in retrospect it seemed predestined.

The circumstances which produced the *Great Eastern* began when gold was discovered in Australia in the year of the Great Exhibition, 1851. This gave a great boost to emigration from Britain and to an already growing commerce between the two countries and with the Orient generally. With an eye to the precedent of the Royal Mail steamship lines to America and the West Indies, the Australian Royal Mail Co was established to achieve a similar steamship service to Australia. Of course, this was not a simple matter; the distance was far in excess of the cruising range of the largest steamships existing and the availability of coal en route, and in Australia, was either doubtful or arranged only at great cost. The sailing ship could accomplish the journey with lower overheads and a greater return, but with a penalty in time and comfort which was significant to the carriage of passengers and mail. The better class of sailing ships frequently completed the journey in from 100 to 120 days and sometimes less. They followed a long route dictated by wind and tide, swinging out towards South America on the way out, then widely round the Cape of Good Hope and via Cape Horn on the return. Some time, often amounting to a quarter of the total, was lost in the Doldrums—in the region of the Equator. This could be obviated by the installation of an engine-driven screw, which also could be useful against contrary winds. The fuel and power plant required for this, however, added bulk and occupied valuable space, and the screw, when not in use, produced considerable resistance to the progress of the ship unless it were disconnected or, better still, raised out of the water. Where time was at a premium, the auxiliary screw sailing ship could be an economic proposition and accomplish the journey to Australia in seventy to eighty days. With a larger employment of steam, even briefer voyages could be achieved, especially if a more direct route was followed in defiance of the prevailing winds. The higher costs involved in this could be prohibitive but might conceivably be offset by a mail contract or subsidy which the improved time and greater regularity would procure. These were the essential considerations of the economics of steamships on the Australian run.

Another route to the East made more attractive by the steamship was that via Egypt. It is intriguing to read an extract from a letter by a Mr Waghorn printed by the *Engineer and Architect's Journal* in 1838, the year of the first crossing of the Atlantic under steam: 'Five years ago there was not a single steam vessel of any nation plying from Egypt; now, those of England, France, Austria and Egypt, number 18 regular opportunities to and fro every month from Alexandria. When will our Government build the "Great Eastern" of 1,500 tons, to go direct (both ways) between Plymouth and Alexandria in fifteen days, with India mails and passengers, and thus keep the French and Austrian lines from our Indian correspondence.

I shall visit Canton via Calcutta, and see if sufficient interest and capital cannot be realized there for the extension of Indian steam navigation to China.'

Here we have the name 'Great Eastern' already being used of a proposed 'large' ship for the Eastern trade. By 1850, of course, the 'extension of Indian steam navigation to China' via Alexandria had become a reality, dominated by the P & O line, a monopoly which came under growing criticism and which also contributed to the circumstances that led to the *Great Eastern*.

The Australian Royal Mail Steamship Company commissioned Brunel to advise them in specifying and contracting for two steamships to establish a fast service between Australia and England. Apart from the fact that the chairman was William Hawes, a family friend of the Brunels and the brother of Benjamin who was married to Brunel's sister, Brunel had some very tangible recommendations for the task. He had been the brains behind the promotion and design of the *Great Western*, the first viable transatlantic steamer, and of the large, iron, screw steamer *Great Britain*, the latter being the largest ship of the time, although she would appear small for a transoceanic ship today. Several years elapsed from the *Great Britain*'s inception to her maiden voyage in 1845, and she was constructed in a dry dock at Bristol by her owners, the Great Western Company, under a committee of works comprising Brunel, Thomas Guppy, a wealthy and inventive mechanical engineer, entrepreneur, and director of the Company, and Captain Claxton, a retired naval officer. The Bristol shipbuilder, William Patterson, served as shipyard manager and was apparently responsible for the ship lines which modern tank tests have shown to be remarkably correct for her speed.[1] She had the misfortune to be run aground off Ireland in 1846 and thus precipitate the collapse of her Company. She was refloated with great trouble and laid up until she was eventually sold in 1851 to Gibbs, Bright and Co who were in the same Australian trade to which Brunel had now to give some thought.

It was well understood that for a given voyage at a given speed, the larger the ship the lower the proportion of her capacity required for her fuel. This was associated with another fact, that the longer the ship of proper shape, the higher the speed it could reach before it encountered the maximum resistance to its passage through the water. This occurred with the onset of wave-making, a curious fact first elucidated by John Scott Russell in the course of his researches into the subject in Edinburgh between 1835–9. He seems to have been the first to perceive that turbulence and wave-making were major sources of energy loss in the passage of a body through water and that the wave-making tendency of a ship could be greatly reduced by giving it hollow, sinusoidal water lines at the entrance, and after lines of cycloidal form. The length of entrance, he reasoned, should be equal to the length of the wave of the desired speed. Hence the higher the desired speed, the longer should be the entrance and hence the longer the hull. It followed that the proportion of entrance to stern run should be about three to two. This, in a nutshell, was Russell's 'wave-line' principle, first publicly pronounced to the British Association in 1837–8 and developed into a detailed report in 1843.

Scott Russell entered the shipbuilding and marine engineering industry as a naval architect and manager of James Caird of Greenock around 1840, then interrupted this career in 1844 to pursue civil engineering and railway engineering journalism in London. From 1845 to 1851 he also served as Secretary of the Royal Society of Arts in which capacity he was responsible for restoring it to health and leading it to the sponsorship of the Great International Exhibition of 1851, on the Royal Commission of which he was appointed joint secretary. When, by 1847, the railway bubble had burst, Russell returned to naval architecture in partnership with Robinson & Co on the Isle of Dogs at Millwall, which firm he took over on the retiral of the Robinsons in 1852, changing its name to J. Scott Russell & Co. The yard, interestingly enough, had formerly belonged to William Fairbairn and was adjacent to that of David Napier, both of whom had abandoned shipbuilding. It was at this juncture that Brunel invited Russell to submit a bid for the two iron screw steamships he had recommended to the Australian Royal Mail Co.

I.K. Brunel was the son of the ingenious engineer Mark Isambard Brunel who fled the French Revolution and finally settled with his English wife in England. After serving with his father, notably in the construction of the Thames tunnel, I.K. Brunel branched out on his own, first with the Clifton Bridge, Bristol, then as engineer of the Great Western Railway. In the latter especially, he gave free rein to his impetuous originality and bold conceptions, of which the most obvious manifestation was the relatively broad gauge of the track and its novel requirements. He was not only the designer but sometimes also the promoter of bold engineering schemes, ever ready to stretch existing technology to the limit, and always with one eye on how it would appear to posterity and redound to his fame. He was aware of commercial constraints but was reluctant to accept them when they interfered with what was ideal in engineering and operational terms. He listened to and used the ideas of those whose expertise he respected, but at the execution level he left very little to the discretion of subordinates. Nothing was too small for his attention, and he restlessly observed, noted, ordered, criticised, and reprimanded, writing letters and memoranda well into the night and requiring but a few hours sleep daily. A supreme commander indeed, and often conducting campaigns on several fronts simultaneously with unquestionable courage and fervour.

Scott Russell and Brunel were certainly well acquainted, and it would be characteristic of Brunel to be attracted to Russell's progressive scientific ideas on iron ship design and construction and not at all surprising that he should favour Russell's bid. It is likely, too, that Russell would be more amenable to Brunel's interference or direct involvement than would a more established and less scientific shipbuilder, a matter of some importance to Brunel who could rarely leave well alone. In this instance, however, he was distracted by a new adventure which the exigencies of the voyage to Australia suggested to him, the nature of which the reader may well guess.

The iron steamships, the *Adelaide* and *Victoria*, which Russell now built to Brunel's specifications had wave-line hulls but were smaller than the *Great Britain* (3,000 tons laden displacement as against 3,675 tons). They were subdivided by watertight bulkheads and two longitudinal bulkheads flanking the engine space, at which location they were attached to an iron deck, forming two great box girders with the side of the ship. The interior of these boxes also served as bunkers. The framing was conventionally transverse but with no projecting keel. The screw could be disconnected from its oscillating engine drive through a clutch mechanism, and the ships were rigged to sail as required. They were intended to complete the whole journey under steam and resort to sail only in very favourable circumstances or in an emergency. This required the maintenance of coal stocks at suitable refuelling points—in this case St Vincent, St Helena and Cape Town—by a fleet of sailing colliers. Averaging a speed of between nine and ten knots, the *Adelaide* and *Victoria* were expected to cut the time of the journey to Australia to sixty days. The fastest iron clippers could attain a much higher speed—about 13 knots—but of course were obliged to take a much longer route in pursuit of favourable winds and currents. With the help of auxiliary screws, these ships, with names like *Morning Cloud* and *Royal Sovereign*, made the journey in seventy days and occasionally even less. They were not comfortable passenger ships, but they could carry a greater pay load of cargo with lower overheads than a steamship of the same size and therefore return a greater profit to the shipowner. It is interesting to note that Brunel's *Great Britain* was being refitted as an auxiliary screw sailing ship and being placed by her new owners on the Australian run at this very time. Following the sailing ship route she made the journey in sixty-five days and returned via Cape Horn in sixty-two.

We can well imagine Brunel, as he studied the pros and cons of the Australian trade, coming round to the inevitable question which, indeed, had been raised before: What were the dimensions of the smallest steamship which would be able to make the round trip from England to Australia without refuelling en route? At first guess it would be about six times the displacement of each of the two new ships under construction in Scott Russell's yard. He communicated his thoughts to Russell and the latter confirmed that they were talking of a ship of at least 18,000 tons displacement and 600ft long for an average economical maximum speed of 14 or 15 knots. The problem in this case would be whether or not the capacity of such a ship would be excessive for the trade.

Brunel was attracted to the challenge of scale; but the ship he was now considering represented an even greater step in the extension of existing technology than did the *Great Britain*. It was a prodigious ship which would enlarge the structural problems of rigidity and strength to an unprecedented degree. What a weight of machinery and boilers would have to be supported and thrown about by the waves.

What great machinery indeed! Certainly the proportion of machinery space required would be less than in smaller steamships but it would be a much heavier load supported on a longer span. How, too, could that great power be delivered? Two sets of paddles? Two screws? One screw and one set of paddles? In March 1852, Brunel entered the latter in his calculation book and opted for it. He did not express reasons for his choice; but it is evident that the requisite power could not easily be delivered through a single screw and that the power plants and screws of the time were too large to allow

The transverse and longitudinal bulkheads, taken on 19 June 1855 (*International Museum of Photography, Rochester, New York*)

By 20 October 1855, when this photograph was taken, the double skin was well advanced. The 'in-and-out' strakes may be clearly seen, as may a row of fire buckets hanging from a beam on the access tower (*International Museum of Photography, Rochester, New York*)

The main deck before launching (*International Museum of Photography, Rochester, New York*)

A group of directors reviewing the difficult tailoring of the stern on 3 December 1857 (*International Museum of Photography, Rochester, New York*)

of twin screws. The screw, however, was superior to paddles in most respects except in the matter of manoeuvrability or navigation under shallow draft. Brunel, therefore, made the best choice of the options open to him. He showed his sketches to Scott Russell, Captain Claxton and the railway magnates, McCalmont and Burke.[2] He set them thinking. As a commercial proposition, who would be interested in it? The Australian Royal Mail Co had supplied its immediate needs with the *Adelaide* and *Victoria* and the first of these was not yet even in the water. It was probably Russell who suggested the Eastern Steam Navigation Co. This company had been formed in the previous year with a nominal capital of £1.2 million in £20 shares, with power to increase to 2 million, to make a bid for the contract to convey mails to India and Australia via Alexandria with unspecified steamships of about 2,000 tons. They had entered into an association with Austrian Lloyds, a company which conducted an efficient service between Trieste and Alexandria, and proposed to compete with the P & O line, which was the company in possession of the mail contract, with faster ships proposed by John Scott Russell and already laid down by him. Although a House of Commons committee had recommended two competing services, and the ESN tender was lower, the Government awarded both services to the P & O line. The ESN Co was thus rudely left without a purpose.

Brunel wrote a paper on the subject of his great ship and submitted it to the directors of the ESN Co who, caught on the rebound as it were, read it with much interest. They arranged for Brunel to address them on the subject, but being unable to attend he asked Scott Russell to substitute for him. This was a fortunate move, for Russell was not associated in people's mind with that taste for the novel and grandiose which could stimulate the fears of the timid or even of the justly cautious. Above all, Russell had an exceptional talent for exposition; abstruse subjects dissolved into their essentials for him and he presented them with great lucidity and charm. Most of the directors liked what they heard Russell say, but some had connected themselves with rival shipping interests or were fearful of Brunel's wilful imagination or were simply not convinced, and these, including the chairman, resigned from the board. One wonders if they ever looked back upon this with wonder or satisfaction at their sagacity or good luck. But high finance was not for the faint-hearted and it tells us much of the spirit of the times that such a fantastic proposition of an iron ship of unimaginable size should receive the support it did.

The proposal placed before the ESN Co directors made the following points. Supposing the ship to sail at the rate of 18 miles per hour, she would make the voyage out to Australia in from thirty to thirty-five days. Averaging the coal consumption at about 182 tons per day, 12,000 tons of coal would then suffice for the round trip. This would cost about £7,200 as against the *Victoria*'s fuelling bill of about £12,000 with a comparatively insignificant pay load. Trade with the Far East, as well as with Australia, was rapidly increasing and was far more significant than that with America. So, too, was the passenger traffic. The prospects for profit seemed undeniably good, and two of the directors in particular, J. Roy Campbell and George T. Braine, financiers of some experience and acumen in the trade, were convinced that provided the combination of capacity and speed could be relied upon, the commercial success of the enterprise was inevitable. Brunel, with some help from his collaborators, set about recruiting new directors favourable to his plan.[3]

The new chairman, H.T. Hope, announced the Company's new objective in appropriately sanguine terms at their half-yearly meeting on 1 December 1852, supported by the independent testimony of some professional men, including the engineers Sir Charles Fox and Joshua Field, and the financier Charles Geach, MP for Coventry, who was chairman of the Midland Bank and a partner in the well-known Yorkshire iron smelters, Messrs Beale & Co, Parkgate Ironworks, Rotherham, Yorkshire, who soon established himself as the financial keystone of the enterprise. It was initially decided that Calcutta should be the terminus and only if expedient, Australia. More than one ship was planned and, certainly, Russell was strongly of the opinion that no shipping line should be started with less than two. The most attractive proposition, however, was to establish a service to Ceylon, a journey the great ships could be expected to complete in thirty days, from which place 'ordinary' steam vessels would radiate to Madras in two days, Calcutta in four, Hong Kong in ten, and Sydney in fourteen. The total time to any of these locations would be a substantial reduction upon the fastest to date, provided, of course, the transfer of freight could be conducted expeditiously. Passengers would present no problems. The expected freight was about 5,000 tons of merchandise with 3,000 passengers at lower fares than those prevailing. A high return of investment, of course, was predicted.

Meanwhile the *Adelaide* and *Victoria*, in that order, had been launched and, by 1853, had entered into service. Both, particularly the *Victoria*, fulfilled expectations but they were commercially dependent upon the mail contract. The proposed great ship, Brunel averred, could pay without a mail contract. But there were dissenters. Some, like Charles Atherton, chief engineer of the Royal Dockyard, Woolwich, did not believe that the proposed ship was actually large enough to accomplish its declared performance of speed and fuel consumption. Others, like W.S. Lindsay, a wealthy shipowner, considered it too large, arguing that there was great commercial disadvantage in delivering large consignments of goods to a market and thus depressing prices. Where, too, were the harbours that such a vessel drawing about 25 ft of water could enter and where enough room for such a necessarily clumsy ship to manoeuvre?

The capitalists interested in the project, however, were not deterred and the shares forfeited by their resigning colleagues were offered to the public. Work was authorized to proceed when 40,000 shares, representing a capital of £800,000, were taken. Bids were called and Brunel recommended the acceptance of Scott Russell's bid for the hull, including its launch, the paddle engines, propeller shaft and the rigging, amounting to £332,295. The hull alone was to cost £275,200, which was slightly in excess of Brunel's own estimate. Brunel persuaded the contractors to accept a plan whereby about a quarter of their payments were to be made in shares and, in Russell's case, 2,000 shares were to be held as security against breach of contract. No one else made a bid for this contract, although the directors were at pains to emphasise the absence of prior commitment, and it is difficult to think of any suitable shipbuilder other than Russell who could have worked with Brunel as a contractor and partner, let alone accept the risks and challenges of unprecedented construction and design problems. The screw engines were allotted to the Watt Co (Soho Works, Birmingham) and the size of the ship was settled at 692ft × 83ft × 58.5ft, 22,500 tons, with a speed of 14 knots. Brunel expected to be able to complete the two proposed ships ready for sea for no more than £500,000 each. How wrong they all were.

As superintendent engineer of the Company Brunel required that all detail designs and drawings should be submitted to him for approval and he authorized payment to the contractors according to his estimate of the work performed. This was the customary practice in railway contracts. In shipbuilding, two payment procedures were known. One was to pay the shipbuilder in advance at certain roughly assessed stages of progress, leaving a final payment to be made on completion. The other, which has been documented for certain shipbuilders in the middle of the nineteenth century, specifies payments in four instalments: when first framed, when plated, when launched and on completion of the trial trip.[4] The latter placed a somewhat greater burden on the shipbuilder's liquidity and in this respect resembles the procedure adopted by Brunel and accepted by Russell. In the case of the *Great Eastern*, the large investment made more frequent payments desirable. Brunel directly related the work done to the weight of iron fastened in place, a somewhat arbitrary index, and assessed this at agreed intervals. Of course, the mode of payment availed nothing if the estimate was short and there was little experience to guide Russell in the costing of such a novel ship. In the circumstances he had reason to have confidence in his financial support. Charles Geach, the wealthiest director, was his principal backer. Brunel, too, as we have noted, corroborated his estimate and in his previous work for Brunel he had experienced no difficulty in having accounted as 'extras' those changes which arose from Brunel's irresistible—and understandable—compulsion to alter the agreed designs, procedures and intentions as the work proceeded. Some of these suggestions or requirements added to the cost of construction, others did not; but Russell, in time, was to find this working to his disadvantage.

From the inception of the proposal, Brunel consulted all— principally Joshua Field and John Scott Russell—who could lend tutored opinions and advice on the various engineering problems it posed. What proportion of power should be allotted the screw and paddles? What steam pressure? What power? Where should the paddles be located? Would steam jacketing such large engine cylinders be worthwhile? He proposed that the cylinder jacket steam be supplied by a high pressure auxiliary boiler (high pressure, 60psi, for high temperatures), and that on leaving the jacket the steam would retain sufficient temperature to enable it to be used to preheat the main steam supply to the engine. He had also found that when a steamship's engines had to be stopped suddenly in an emergency, the deafening noise of excess steam being blown off was very distressing and alarming to passengers. This he thought could be mitigated by the insertion of wire gauze in the blow off pipes.

He considered also the grouping of the boiler tubes, through which the hot flue gases passed, such that they could be removed for cleaning without shutting down the boilers. The accumulation of scale on the heating surfaces, especially since sea water was used for make-up, was a great source of boiler inefficiency. Removable tube bundles, however, would have demanded a radical change in the design of the boilers with all the risks of failure, and the idea was not pursued further, nor has it ever been found practicable. Combustion tests were conducted on a mock-up of a single furnace of the intended boilers to discover to what extent various kinds of coal could economically be used, and other experiments were carried out to determine the possible advantage of steam jacketing the paddle engine cylinders. The results of the latter did not overcome the objections of Russell and Field (and with such large cylinders they were probably right) and Brunel therefore reluctantly abandoned this idea also. Illumination by acetylene gas generated on board was proposed and was in fact adopted, but on a more limited scale than originally planned. Likewise diluted was the proposal to heat or cool the principal apartments with forced air delivered by ducts from deck or boiler room—air conditioning in fact. A preparation for making wood non-inflammable was also tested, but the result is not known. Brunel was indefatigable in the pursuit of useful and progressive ideas, others might call them novelties, and took great note of the experiences of others which would help him avoid pitfalls and achieve improvements. In the event, very few even of the most practical of his proposals were to be realized. It took all the resources of engineering skill and finance to produce the ship without them.

Transcending all these flights of technological fancy was the imperative challenge of the structural design of such a long ship with a great weight of machinery amidships. The bending, hogging and twisting of long, laden ships on the high seas, about numerous possible axes, was a daunting prospect. Russell had already coped successfully with this on a smaller scale in certain shallow-draught iron steam boats he had been called upon to design for service in river and coastal waters. In these he had resorted to a system of longitudinal framing and partial and full bulkheads. It is to be expected that Russell would consider an extension of the same techniques in the design of the great new ship now before him. Whether Brunel discussed this subject with Russell is unknown, but it is likely that it did arise. Gradually, as Brunel pondered over the various structural problems, including the idea of an outer skin of wood which could be coppered and thus prevent fouling by barnacles, he came round to the idea of sandwiching the longitudinal girders of the ship between an inner and outer hull, in a way that was analogous to the top and bottom of the Stephenson-Fairbairn tube, called the Britannia Tube after the bridge which inspired it.

This long iron tube was developed in the 1840s by Robert Stephenson and Fairbairn to bridge the Menai Strait in Wales for the steam trains of the Chester–Holyhead Railway. It was rectangular and extremely long—400ft—essentially comprising a line of girders along the floor and another line along the roof. The girders were sandwiched between layers of plating, and roof and floor were rigidly connected together by the plated sides of the tube. This gave great strength with minimum weight and suggested an ample answer to the structural problems of the great ship. Transverse webs intersecting the longitudinal girders of the ship gave the impression of a kind of honeycomb of cells between the two hulls, hence the term 'cellular construction' which was often used of it. With longitudinal bulkheads flanking the engine space, transverse watertight bulkheads and 'wave' lines, the ship to all appearances was a scaled-up version of the *Victoria* or *Adelaide*, with the addition of a double hull and a double iron deck.

Before a plate could be laid, the method of launching had to be decided. Russell was attracted to the idea of building the ship in a dock, and two or three sites for this were suggested. But the requisite size of this dry dock and the difficulties of constructing it, especially in the mud and gravel of the Isle of Dogs, presented problems of time and cost. Brunel, having more experience in earthworks, made an estimate of that cost and decided that it was prohibitive.[5] The figure £20,000 appears in his calculation book, including a £2000 contingency,[6] which seems an incredible underestimate in comparison with some other known costs, but which may be for the excavation only. The costs of the alternative, of constructing above ground without proper cranes, and of launching, should have been placed against it. But nearly everything would have been underestimated, we can be sure. Russell and Brunel then agreed upon a broadside launch. A lengthwise launch would have required the bow of the ship to be raised such that the height of the forecastle would be over 100ft from the ground, which, in the absence of tall cranes, would have occasioned much difficulty. But perhaps even more persuasive was the concern about the overstraining of the hull at that stage of the launch at which the stern would become waterborne while her bow was still on the launching ways. It should be remembered that, on account of the lack of dockyard and crane facilities, her engines and boilers had to be installed while she was on the stocks, thus placing a considerable deadweight amidships. Brunel was also strongly of the opinion that the ship should be lowered gradually to the low-water mark in a controlled fashion, then floated off. He had in mind the possibility of constructing a patent slip, utilizing wheels or rollers, a slip and mechanical apparatus which could then be transferred to the home port of the ship where it could be used to haul her out of the water for repairs.

To avoid blocking his whole waterfront, Russell leased part of the adjacent shipyard from David Napier, and it was in this that the ship was laid down at a convenient distance above high-water mark. Had Napier's yard not been available, Russell could not easily have accepted a broadside launch as it would have prevented his taking other contracts.

A vast number of timber piles, 24ft long, were pounded into the earth to form a solid support for the great hull and her launching ways. Those supporting the ship were left protruding 4ft above ground. Many new devices and machines, for cutting, rolling, punching and riveting, were designed and constructed, and railway track was laid down for transporting the iron plates and fittings.

The immense paddle engines, the largest ever built, comprised four cast-iron cylinders moulded and cast in Russell's foundry and bored and faced in his machine shop. The crankshaft was forged by Fulton and Neilson at the Lancefield Forge in Glasgow, the largest forgings then attempted anywhere and demanding the installation of larger steam hammers and other equipment. The Lancefield Forge was the progenitor of the celebrated Parkhead Forge of William Beardmore, situated, of course, in Parkhead, a suburb of Glasgow; which, incidentally, was Scott Russell's birthplace and the home of his immediate ancestors. Everything connected with the great ship demanded new tools, new techniques, and enlarged facilities of all kinds. Russell also had to acquire a lathe large enough to machine the crankshaft and propeller shaft forgings when they arrived from Glasgow.

It was originally anticipated that the great ship would be ready for launching eighteen months from the beginning of construction, that is, in October 1855, the keel plate being laid in May 1854.

The planning of the construction of the great ship left little to be desired. As much was standardized and replicated as possible. The plates were of three sizes—1 in on the bottom, ¾ in on the sides and ½ in on deck and bulkheads. There was, of course, no electric welding at this early period, everything was attached by riveting, and the rivets, too, were standardized. Each hull plate was shaped by means of hand-operated rolls and was cut by steam-operated shears, all in accordance with wooden patterns taken from lines which in their turn were taken from a wooden model or models of the hull. Every plate was marked and numbered on the model. A boy painted the positions of the rivet holes using another template and the holes were made by a steam punch. The plate was then transported on a bogie to the site where it had to be lifted by primitive block and tackle to its position, clamped or bolted in place and hand riveted.

The bulkheads and inner skin were fitted first, then the longitudinals and webs to which the outer skin was riveted. Each riveting squad comprised two riveters, one 'holder-on' and two boys—one to heat the rivets and the other to insert the rivet in the hole. When the outer skin was being riveted, the holder-on and his boy were often passing whole days and weeks in the confined space between the hulls (2ft 10in) with little light other than from a candle and enduring the deafening thunder of the riveters' hammers. It is from this that the story arose of the rivet boy being sealed into the double bottom. These cells were also painted to reduce corrosion. There were three million rivets in the finished ship and 30,000 hull plates, most of which were of the maximum size which could economically be rolled at the time—10ft × 2.75ft × 1in thick—and were lugged and lifted without the aid of cranes.

There was anything but a blaze of publicity attending the start of work on the great ship. Little was popularly known about it until, towards the end of 1854, a description in *The Builder* was widely reproduced. This made a dramatic comparison between the ship and the houses in Tavistock Square. At last the immensity of the vessel could more easily be comprehended, and gradually, as she rose above or out of the mud of the Isle of Dogs, she drew more and more attention nationally as well as locally.

Within the confines of the shipyard, however, problems had begun to grow. The system of seeking the superintendent engineer's approval of every drawing, and considering and implementing his amendments or changes of mind was time consuming. This, along with the many novel erecting problems to be solved, was sufficient to retard progress, so that by the close of 1854, it was evident that the ship would not be ready for launching in eighteen months as planned. In his report to the directors, Brunel generously accepted most of the blame, justifying it on the grounds of establishing a better procedure which would show benefits later.[7]

On top of this, however, in November 1854, Charles Geach unexpectedly died. Since he was a substantial backer of the Scott Russell Co and the great ship, his loss was serious. Especially, too, since he had undertaken to accept shares from Russell—who was substantially paid in shares—in payment for iron from Beale Iron Works of which he was a director. The Company entered into a new arrangement in its payments to Russell to help meet this difficulty, but as 1855 progressed, the increased demand for materials and skilled labour occasioned by the exigencies of the current war in the Crimea, inflated prices and wages. It is hardly surprising, therefore, that Russell found it necessary, that summer, to advise Brunel that he would require about £40,000 in excess of his contract price to see the ship in the water.

The same inflationary strains, unfortunately, were also affecting the shareholders, especially when, towards the close of the year, the war drew to an end, accompanied by a recession in trade, resulting in a much reduced need of new ships, a tight money market and persistent high prices. Many of the shareholders could not or would not meet their calls, which, in turn, threw a burden upon the willing shareholders who, not surprisingly, resented it. The Company reassured them that action was being taken to recover these arrears where possible. Unfortunately, where this was not possible, the forefeited shares could not be sold on the market without further depressing their value. Most shareholders were averse to frequent calls and, indeed, it was stipulated in the prospectus of the Company that calls could not be more frequent than once every three months, and that no call could exceed £2 10s per share. It was this fact which fundamentally controlled the rate of progress.

Another factor, of course, was the effort made by Russell and his men. Brunel therefore applied himself to extracting as much as possible from the latter to the Company's advantage and to resisting Russell's appeals for more generous treatment. Russell then tried to persuade Brunel to authorize payment for the many 'extras' to which he felt entitled. Unfortunately, this could only have unwelcome implications for Brunel. It was bad enough for him to ask the directors for more money in the circumstances without having to admit that any part of the necessity arose from his own notorious, if under-standable, penchant for change or improvement. Yet Brunel could see, at least by November 1855, that Russell had over-extended his financial resources, hardly difficult to do in the prevailing economic circumstances, which were leading to the impending closure of many Thames shipyards. Indeed this period marked the beginning of the end of shipbuilding on the Thames.

Brunel turned a deaf ear to Russell's entreaties, presumably con-vinced that Russell was not producing enough for his money. But Russell was running short of capital and had too much of it locked up in shares of the great ship, shares which had lost value—if they had any value at all. In January 1856, the crisis in Russell's affairs came to a head and the directors of the ESN Company were persuaded that they had to make some effort to revise his contract. The same lawyer and accountant served both parties, and tried to work out a way to keep Russell in business while at the same time serving the best interests of the Company.

Exacerbating this to some extent was a disagreement between Russell and Brunel on whether the launch should be free or con-trolled. Russell, fortified by the recommendations of G.W. Bull, a shipbuilder on the Great Lakes, had come down in favour of a free launch while Brunel resolutely adhered to his original but more ex-pensive plan to lower the ship gradually into the water. Under the contract, Russell was responsible for the cost and execution of the launch and all risks attending it. Brunel was of the opinion that Russell's best plan was to liquidate voluntarily under inspectorship and thus avoid possible bankruptcy, then devote himself exclusively to the engineering part of his business.[8] Perhaps under this convic-tion, or because the negotiations were not going to his liking, or because of private information, Brunel, at the beginning of February 1856, advised the Company to take possession of the ship on grounds of breach of contract and thus protect the ship from seque-stration in the event of Russell's failure, whereupon the bankers fore-closed on Russell's property and refused to honour his cheques. That settled it. The bankers, of course, would note that the ESN Co was in trouble too, with arrears in calls on shares amounting to £149,300.

Only four years before, Russell had set out on his own as a ship-builder with high hopes and bold enterprise; now, despite all his talent, he was on the verge of bankruptcy. Brunel endured some

28

odium for Russell's fate and it is not easy with the meagre information at our disposal to pass categorical judgement on the matter. The evidence clearly establishes, however, that both Brunel and Russell underestimated the cost of the project and that Russell started upon it with certain reassuring presumptions which, to his cost, proved to be ephemeral. When Brunel refused to accept Russell's arguments for more money, he could expect the support of the directors, under pressure as they were, and avoid their criticism of himself. In defence he complained to the directors that Russell had increasingly ignored his instructions and demands and that the method of launching which Russell now alleged was going to be more expensive than he expected had been agreed upon from the start. Some, including John Fowler (of Forth Bridge fame), later held the opinion that Brunel had treated Russell badly, and Russell is reported to have attributed this to jealousy,[9] presumably of Russell's growing public identification with the great ship, and indeed the issue of credit for the great ship continued to be raised from time to time.

But Russell had not yet been cut off from the enterprise; he was directed by the liquidators to negotiate a price for the completion of the ship on their behalf. Brunel, however, was not happy with this and contrived, although unsuccessfully, to go it alone with Russell's foremen and even with Russell as an assistant, an expedient upon which the liquidators, and Russell, looked askance. The bankers drove a hard bargain for the use of the yard and facilities, and it was only after several weeks of negotiation that a settlement was reached, under the terms of which the liquidators undertook to complete the ship for launching with Russell serving as shipyard manager under the administration of John Yates, the indefatigable company secretary.

Work was recommenced in May, and for the next three months progress was steady. Brunel was ill during part of this time and it appears that Yates and Russell pushed on with much of the work without referring to Brunel for sanction or approval to the extent that he demanded. One wonders if his health was not partly to blame for his irascibility. He suddenly and most querulously found fault with Russell and Yates, accusing them of subverting his proper authority, and, early in September, he forced his dispute before the board. Russell reported that he had pushed on the work as he had undertaken to do, had dealt courteously with Brunel's dictates and had set the work on such a footing that he could now take the month's vacation which he had warned the board would be his desire at that stage of the task.[10] It appeared to the board that the only way to placate Brunel was to dismiss Russell. This, however, was not exactly what Brunel wanted. He wanted absolute control, but he knew he needed a shipyard manager acceptable to the foremen concerned. Yates, fortunately, agreed to continue as business manager as long as the work would not be held up for 'every trifling circumstance' and provided Brunel would not occasion incidental expenditures beyond £20. He also required assurance that his terms of reference would be respected by Brunel, who in turn felt that the board did not appreciate the extent of the burden he had been carrying and the onerous additional responsibilities they were now imposing upon him. On the other hand he thought matters were better ordered under his direct command. We do not know what Russell felt or thought. We can assume that he felt abused by Brunel and that Brunel felt equally abused, although as much at the hands of the directors as of Russell. Scott Russell did not quarrel with Brunel; but one suspects that some, including Brunel, might have been happier if he had defended himself more vociferously.

On his return from his month's vacation, he went about his business as a consultant naval architect and procured the unused portion of David Napier's yard, the other portion being occupied by the *Great Eastern*, in the hope of making a recovery as a shipbuilder, possibly with the aid of an Admiralty contract for one of the iron warships he designed and advocated. It would not be easy for him to look indifferently upon the great ship with which he had been so intimately involved at all stages of projection, design and construction, being completed by his own men in what had been his own yard, under the direction of the man whom he would regard as largely responsible for his predicament.

As work progressed, so too did calls on the shares. The financial picture was disturbing—£450,000 had been expended on the ship by February 1857. The arrears of calls amounted to £192,000 of which only about £64,000 was thought recoverable. A total of £642,000, therefore, had been called, leaving a balance of £158,000. One of the retiring directors, John McCalmont, declared that a further £60,000 in addition to the available share capital would be required to complete the ship for sea with reasonable equipment, and he was very nervous about meeting further calls on his shares until it was known if and how the further funds were to be raised. The Company ignored this and confidently expected that any further funds could more easily be raised after the launch, now planned for August. As a feeble help to the depleted funds, visitors were admitted to the yard at lunchtime each day and from 3.30 to 4.30 on Saturday afternoons, for 2/6d. River steamers and horsedrawn omnibuses carried loads of eager sightseers to and fro and many greatly doubted that the great hulk would ever be moved. Their apprehensions seemed confirmed when the launch was again postponed while the bankers in possession of the property made difficulties over the extension of the lease. Again they drove a very hard bargain. The tough world of high finance was cannibalistic.

Pressure was now exerted on Brunel to launch the ship without delay. He had subcontracted the launching cradles and ways and had abandoned his idea of the patent slip on account of its expense in the face of the soaring costs. This left him with what he regarded as a troublesome problem—the possibility of the elimination of the lubrication of the ways as the ship progressed on its controlled descent, leading to the binding of wood on wood, especially at high spots on the uneven bearing surfaces. He feared that a stoppage from such a cause would be disastrous, occasioning a ruinous expenditure of money for correction, of the order, he thought, of £50,000. His solution to this problem was to line the underside of the cradles with strips of iron, parallel to the axis of the ship, and to top the launching ways with rows of iron rails, common railway track, running down to the river. He had William Froude conduct some experiments which appeared to confirm the feasibility of this expedient as far as frictional resistance was concerned.

The alternative was a free launch, but Brunel considered this potentially dangerous to the hull, despite the reassurances of Mr Bull. It would have required some dredging near the river bank and control of the traffic on the river. He thought the idea ridiculous. The controlled launch, he believed, assured the safety of the ship, provided, of course, that the launching ways were well founded and would not sink under the weight of the ship even if it should halt part way, no small proviso. He believed that his iron rails would obviate the adhesion problem; what a shock awaited him.

The bearing area of each of the two cradles supporting the ship, wood on wood, would have been 120 × 80ft, increased from the original 80 × 80ft, that is, a total weight of about 12,000 tons would

31

have been supported on a total area of 19,200 sq ft, giving an average bearing pressure of about 0.6 tons per square foot, much less than the 2 tons per square foot commonly allowed in free launches in more recent times.

The two ways were constructed to slope, at an incline of about 1 in 12 for 250ft to the low-water mark. A 140ft middle portion of the ship between the cradles was unsupported. The ground was reinforced with timber piles running in five rows under each launching way. Balks of timber were bolted to the tops of the outer and inner rows of piles and between these and over the whole area of the ways was laid a 1ft thick bed of concrete. On top of the concrete were fastened further rows of balks running down the slope, and between these a further layer of concrete to the level of their tops. On this surface a floor of balks was fixed, running parallel to the ship, upon which rails were fastened transversely, with a slight camber across each of the ways to allow for settlement.

Each cradle was restrained by a heavy chain of 60lb links wound round a 9ft diameter reel, 20ft long, from which it could be payed out. The reel, or drum, was well and truly anchored to a cluster of piles. A band brake encircled each of the great flanges of the reels, tightened by means of a long lever on which force was applied as desired through block and tackle by a squad of men, pulling and re-laxing in the manner of a tug-o-war team in response to flag signals from an overseer. The two overseers, one to each drum, were to respond to signals from Brunel perched high on a special little plat-form attached to the side of the ship at main deck level. For those who understood the dangers and difficulties, the system was hair raising even if there were no mechanical failures. A further set of signals was required if the cradles needed some impulse to start them. For this purpose four cables were run from the middle of the ship to wind-lasses on each of four lighters anchored about 100yd in the river. Each windlass could exert a pull of about 60 tons. Then, at bow and stern, pairs of chains were threaded from the ship round pulleys aboard another pair of lighters, back to steam winches ashore. Altogether a force of 600 tons was expected to be exerted by this system, much depending upon the security of the anchors of the light-ers; Brunel's initial calculations suggested that a force of 300 tons would suffice.[11] Ideally the aim was a just counterpoise of impelling force and constraint uniformly applied to keep the ship moving gently with both cradles in line. A very tall order even if all the personnel involved were experienced in their novel tasks. What panic would be created should one of the drums be unseated or the brake give way while the other held or did not hold.

Brunel had some experience of concerted haulage operations through the raising of his Saltash Bridge and had observed the like operation conducted by Robert Stephenson in the raising of his long girders across the Menai Straits, but hazardous as these were, they seem straightforward when compared to the launching of the *Great Eastern*.

Brunel's anxieties at this time cannot be exaggerated. 'Launch the ship', exhorted Yates early in October, 'or we shall be in the hands of the Philistines.' 'I shall not be hurried', responded Brunel, but he made haste nevertheless. The contractor of the ways had exceeded his deadline and there was insufficient time to have everything and everybody well prepared and the haulage system tested. Every day added to the mounting expense. Brunel must by now have had some sympathy for Russell, realizing full well that he had underestimated the cost of the launch and that he and Russell had together grossly underestimated their contract. At the end of October he bent to circumstances and decided to attempt the launch on the spring tide of 3 November.

2
THE LAUNCH

As the launch day approached, all the restraining shores and encumbrances were removed from the hull and work on the cradles and ways continued to the very last. The preparations involved an army of from 1,000 to 1,500 workmen who, when darkness fell, took on the appearance of strange, ant-like figures leaping and waving in the gas flares which had hurriedly been installed, accompanied by the clangour of action, the shouts of orders and the chants of 'heave-o'. Brunel, Scott Russell and Harrison, the appointed captain of the ship, were observed conferring among themselves and directing this nocturnal army on the night before the launch. When the dawn of the great day broke through an overcast sky and curtains of drizzle, the great and shapely hull was revealed ready for her début, with a copper-coloured stripe round her middle, separating black above and red lead below. Temporary galleries seemed to have sprouted everywhere, along the quays and on the tops of workshops and houses. Inside the yard itself accommodation was prepared for the privileged spectators. Brunel was peculiarly vexed at this. He would have preferred to have accomplished the whole operation quietly, free from the fear of failure and of misunderstanding by the ignorant multitude. But the word got out, despite denials, and to Brunel's chagrin, the directors sold 3,000 tickets for admission to the yard.

Greater crowds would have gathered had the repeated postponements of the launch not deterred the more sceptical, but the vendors and the showmen did not seem to be caught unprepared—Punch and Judy, the six-legged sheep, the performing dog and all the familiar characters of the fair lined the approaches. Even by ten o'clock, several bands purveyed somewhat inebriated music at different pubs. The environs of the shipyards on the Isle of Dogs seemed at their best in the rain, for sunlight and squalor are somehow incompatible, and the gutters dripped drearily over the crowded and

John Scott Russell, FRS, c.1860 (*Royal Institution of Naval Architects*)

Isambard Kingdom Brunel standing by the chains of the stern checking drum used to control the rate of launch in 1857 (*Brunel University Library*)

ways restraining the ship. The lighters on the river, in response to a
signal, accordingly hauled their tackle more taut, but, after about ten
minutes, it was evident that this was insufficient to overcome the
initial adhesion. Dickson then, according to plan, ordered a slight
pressure to be exerted by the hydraulic rams upon the cradles. Suddenly, the forward cradle slipped slowly, accompanied by a loud
united shout, moving about three or four feet in two seconds, and
had nearly come to rest when the hull quivered from stem to stern
and the after cradle followed with a grinding and sullen roar, slipping about six feet. As it did so, it jerked in the slack on the brake
drum, thus spinning the take-up windlass and scattering or hurling
into the air five or six men who had been holding or leaning on its
handle. The crew of the near brake panicked and fled but the crew on
the other brake stood firm. The crews on the middle barges on the
river also panicked when the ship moved, one of their number
actually jumping into a small boat and shoving off. It was generally
assumed that the brakes had stopped the ship, but at least one foot of
slack was reported to have been seen between the cradles and the
drums at the end of the slide.[1] The injured workmen, some unconscious, were carried to a nearby pub thence to Poplar hospital. One,
an Irish labourer of seventy-five was the most seriously hurt. He
apparently was not a member of the official crew of the windlass and
had been partially seated on a handle when it unexpectedly sprang
into life. The old fellow, tough as he must have been, succumbed
after a few days.

This accident unnerved the participants and it took an hour or
thereabouts to restore calm and reorganize. To add to the difficulties, the rain now descended in a steady drizzle. Nevertheless, another
start was made and considerable force was exerted through the end
cables and the rams for some minutes without result when suddenly
there was a resounding crash from the forward cradle accompanied
by a scatter of people in the vicinity. Another accident? Fortunately
not; a careful inspection revealed nothing amiss, but it did not relieve
the tension which must now have been mounting to uncomfortable
levels. Some teeth on the gears of the forward winch stripped, and
then a pin broke in one of the rams. Brunel must have been very glad
to call it a day, as, too, the soaked, weary and apprehensive onlookers. Some scrambled everywhere to have a closer look at things and
others melted away like snow off a dyke, and the unfeeling world
laughed at the spectacle of Brunel left with a giant ship he could not

get into the water. It was expected by many, of course, that he would succeed next day or the day after, but Brunel knew that more force was going to be required and that he therefore could no longer expect to catch the present spring tides. If friction alone were the foe, it could easily be estimated that a force of about 1,400 tons would be necessary, taking a coefficient of friction of 0.2, or 1,600 tons with a coefficient of 0.3. The rams and haulage gear were barely able to cope with this. The Prince Consort dropped in to see the ship on 6 November, as occasionally did the directors and their friends.

Since the crews of the barges hauling the ship from the river were apparently unreliable, Brunel moved the winches from the barges to the landward side of the ship and used the barges to support sheaves round which the cables or chains from the ship were threaded, thence under the ship's bottom to the winches. The barges were also moored more securely to the opposite bank of the river and an additional 10in press was applied to each cradle. It was estimated that the four presses could apply a total force of 800 tons, and, since the ship had been moved with much less force in the first instance, it was expected that this would be adequate.

An attempt to move the ship with the new gear was made on 19 November, but the abutments for the rams gave way. The piling of the abutments was then reinforced and more securely bound to share the load; but the river tackle remained a perplexing source of trouble. Some of the mooring chains parted at loads much below their rated capacity, and fishing them from the bed of the river was a troublesome task often complicated by the interruptions of dense fogs. Hanging over Brunel's mind too was the importance of moving the ship clear of the building platform in one substantial move. There was real fear that if the ship should stick with one part rigidly supported on the building platform while the other was more flexibly supported on the weaker foundation of the launching ways, the latter would settle and cause deformations of the ship which could perhaps overstress its structure in places.

Brunel now regretted abandoning his plan to use a specially devised hydraulic apparatus which would push the ship continuously down the ways. It would, of course, have been difficult for him to explain before his present trouble why this additional expenditure was more necessary than it had been when he made his original estimate and held Russell to the undertaking of a controlled launch with a price tag of £14,000.

Now with the certain prospect of having to push the ship foot by foot down the slope mainly by rams, several new problems arose. Once the ship moved beyond the reach of the rams, timbers had to be used as distance pieces until the rams themselves and their abutments were brought closer to the cradles. Any long sojourn of the hull on the launching ways raised the possibility of unequal settlement, leading to a continuous 'uphill' struggle out of perpetual hollows and to possible damage. This, after all, was the launching method which Brunel had preferred on account of its 'greater safety'. He was anxious on this score and he therefore checked a portion of the ways for settlement under a load of about one ton per square foot imposed by 100 tons of scrap iron spread over an area of 10sq ft. The result reassured Brunel but it told him nothing about local stresses where the metal runners rested on the rails and bedded into them. But it was in a more optimistic frame of mind that he continued operations on Saturday 28 November.

As though to reward him for his pains, the ship moved steadily at about one inch a minute, first the forward cradle, then the after, until a halt was called around midday for dinner. On resuming operations, the ship refused to be moved. It was noted that the rails were pressing about one inch into the wood supporting them and that the cradles were, in effect, nestling in slight hollows in places. The river tackle was again troublesome and, when two out of the four midship barges broke their mooring chains, everyone was relieved to call a halt to a miserable cold day in the mud. A total of 14ft was chalked up on the blackboards used to record movements.

The broken chains were pieced together in the night and the moorings replaced. Operations were resumed next day, although this was a Sunday, but two of the mooring chains broke again and the chain attached to the stern dragged its 15 ton mooring block of granite all the way across the bed of the river until it was high and dry under the ship's stern. Two heavy timber battering rams shod with iron were then applied to the cradles in addition to the presses but to no effect.

Brunel had set up a field command headquarters in a rude canvas shelter commanding a good view of the works and from thence, with his field glasses round his neck, issued orders and received reports through his aide-de-camp, his son Henry. After the loss of the river tackle, he decided to augment his hydraulic jacks with all the jacks, both screw and hydraulic, which could be scrounged from the yard and neighbouring works. This whole battery was ordered into action and moved the ship at last, about one inch per second, for a total of about eight feet before darkness fell.

Next day the siege was continued with the same forces and the same progress until about eight and a half feet were chalked up, at which stage a 10in jack on the forward cradle burst. The progress, alas, was most disappointing and in a desperate effort to catch the next spring tide on 2 December, Brunel employed two more hydraulic jacks upon each cradle in addition to replacing the broken jack, and further strengthened the moorings of the barges upon the opposite bank of the river.

The press and public anticipated the deliberate effort which was now made on Thursday 3 December to catch the spring tide, and surprisingly large crowds gathered at many vantage points, including a large scaffold erected between the gables of two houses near the yard. Numerous boats lent a festive air to the river and an unusual number of distinguished visitors congregated to view the events of the day. Fortunately, there was progress, the ship jerking down immediately in spurts of about a foot. Scarcely had the operations started, however, when a loud crash accompanied by cries and screams announced the collapse of the scaffolding outside the gates. About 200 people were dropped a distance of 20ft into a confused heap but, miraculously, no one was killed, although many were injured and seven found their way to Poplar hospital. Taking no more than a look over his shoulder, as it were, Brunel pushed on with his advance and by dusk the ship had moved about 14ft. Now when the ship moved, it did so in long quick jerks rather than steadily, the strain energy built up in the abutments being relieved as soon as movement reduced the frictional resistance; making the whole yard tremble.

By this time Brunel was being bombarded with advice from all and sundry and from all parts of the country. He had a standard acknowledgement printed and sent in reply to every such correspondent. On being tipped off that Robert Stephenson was feeling a little upset at not being invited to visit the operations, Brunel immediately sent off the necessary note. The Company tried to encourage its anxious shareholders by publishing a prediction of their anticipated profits, if only the ship were in service.

What was now considered good progress was continued on 4 December, until the skewing of the hull seemed to lock it again in an immovable position. After much vain huffing and puffing and the failure of two rams of 14in and 7in, and despite the buoyant effect of the high tide lapping the hull to a depth of 4ft, the siege was abandoned for the day.

Next day, the Saturday, proved even less fruitful, despite the encouraging but brief presence of the Princess Royal, the Duchess of Atholl and party and the enthusiastic support of the Marquis of Stafford, Sir Joseph Paxton (the celebrated gardener-cum-architect of the Duke of Devonshire) and others. The ship was too far away from the rams; the extent of the timber strutting transmitting their action to the cradles had reached an impossible 60ft. New abutments for the rams were quickly built and much was being said in the papers of the improved anchorages accorded by Trotman's new patent anchors. When operations were resumed on the Monday, the water supply pipes of two rams burst and it was afternoon before any progress was made and that very slight. When the unavailing force on the cradles was released the hull capriciously slipped a further 2ft. The procedure, of course, was to overcome the static resistance with the rams, then keep the hull moving with the haulage gear. Two or three more slips were obtained but the mooring tackle of the haulage gear began to give way yet again, and, to crown all, a heavy fog now enveloped the river.

The desperate effort to clear the ship from the yard and save the Company the December lease, amounting to £1,000, was in vain. The crucial tide was missed for another month. The strain upon Brunel was immense; this was the most harrowing ordeal of his professional life. He now tried to make absolutely certain of the troublesome moorings of the barges, had heavy piles driven into the opposite bank of the river and bedded the anchors into them. Meantime the ship settled into its new position and rust developed on the iron surfaces.

Robert Stephenson, now in very poor health, visited the yard and gave moral support to his troubled professional friend. He had no original expedient to suggest, but approved the application of further brute force, probably now the most simple and economical procedure feasible. There is a moving photograph of Stephenson with Brunel in a group with Lord Alfred Paget, and John Yates taken at Brunel's tent in the yard which expresses a great deal without words.

Stephenson was with Brunel on 16 December when all systems were ready for the greatest heave to date, nearly 2,000 tons. About

3ft were chalked up for that day's work, but at the expense of the whole siegeworks; several rams, windlasses and chains being broken in succession. The drum of one windlass was crushed, to the wonder of all, and a 10in ram gave warning of distress by weeping through its 6in thick cast-iron cylinder before ripping apart. The unprecedented array of force was awesomely reduced until there was scarcely anything left with which to push or pull. It was a low ebb in the long struggle. The cost of the launch, first an optimistic £14,000, then £25,000, was now hovering around £100,000. The editor of *The Engineer* wrote: 'This launch has no interest in an engineering point of view, because it is known that with sufficient force and sufficient fulcrum, this or any other bulk may be moved.' The principal difficulties, he believed, were due to irregularities or flexible waves in the surface of the ways interlocking with others in the under-surface of the cradles. John Scott Russell attributed most of the trouble to excessive local bearing stresses deforming the surfaces of contact and causing the runners to bite into the rails when the lubrication was rubbed off. The skewing of the cradles on the ways, which were cambered, increased the force required as also did flexure of the rails, especially when the load was allowed time to settle. Even more force was expected to be necessary after the long delay following the failure of 16 December.

Several new rams were therefore purchased from Messrs Tangye of Birmingham and the largest ram cast to that time, one used in the raising of the Britannia Bridge, was secured. Eleven rams in all, braced against new piled abutments—which must have required the laborious breaking of the thick concrete of the ways—were applied to the aft cradle and ten to the forward. The haulage gear, too, was even more securely anchored to the Deptford side of the river; but a barque running up river on 4 January 1858 collided with one of the barges and sank it. It is a wonder this had not already happened more than once. Nevertheless, while Captain Harrison set about re-establishing the haulage arrangements, steps were taken to heave the ship a sixth time. But a severe frost froze the water in the rams and their supply pipes, requiring about thirty fires maintained day and night to thaw them out. The new rams were equipped with relief valves and pressure gauges which made it possible to prevent the bursts and overstressing which had plagued their precursors. A total force of 4,000 tons could now be exerted, much more than the maximum resistance of about 1,900 tons hitherto encountered.

Brunel, seriously ill, standing by the forward paddle boiler funnel in September 1859 just before the *Great Eastern*'s maiden voyage (*Brunel University Library*)

The only photograph of Brunel and Russell together. Taken by Robert Howell on the occasion of the first attempted launch, on 3 November 1857, it shows from left to right: Scott Russell, H. Wakefield (one of Brunel's staff), Brunel, and Thomas Tredwell, who was awarded the contract for the launching ways and cradles (*Royal Photographic Society*)

An eloquent photograph of Brunel (holding binoculars) supervising the difficult launch from his improvised tent, supported by the ailing Robert Stephenson (seated left), Lord Alfred Paget (with umbrella) and, in front, his son Henry Brunel (left) and John Yates, the company secretary (*Liverpool Museum*)

Drawing closer to the river on 5 December 1857 (*International Museum of Photography, Rochester, New York*)

The river-side of the ship on 30 November 1857. The connection of the tow-chains from the ship to the barges can be seen (*International Museum of Photography, Rochester, New York*)

Another spring tide was allowed to pass and every sinew was to be strained to catch the spring tide at the end of the month. A good start was made on 5 and 6 January by squaring up the ship on the ways and, with good moves of 20ft on 11 and 12 January, the launch of the great ship was at long last assured. Captain Harrison and Henry Brunel rowed round the ship on eight feet of water to the cheers of the workmen. One or two further nudges and the *Leviathan* was in position to float off. At the same time an ominous announcement appeared in *The Times* that the Company was seeking power to increase its capital beyond the original limit of £1,200,000.

The *Leviathan*'s flotation was set for Saturday 30 January, but as that day dawned the wind blew with such strength that Captain Harrison ruled the operation too risky and had the ship well held down with water ballast in her tanks. Brunel had the great foresight to have previously arranged with meteorological observers at Portsmouth and Liverpool to telegraph periodic reports of the weather. The next day, however, was as gentle and fair as the previous one had been grey and stormy. The ballast was pumped out and as the tide rose the rams did their last duty by thrusting the monster and cradles a further few feet into the river. By half past one, the ship was seen to be riding free of the cradles, the latter, of course, being weighted to stay submerged. Two tugs fore and aft took the *Leviathan* in hand and moved her gently. The sight produced fervent cheers. But the troubles were not over.

One of the paddlewheels became entangled with the cradles. The debris from the cradles littered the water and from time to time great timber balks leaped to the surface with much force. No sooner was the ship cleared of this than some clumsy navigation ran one of her paddle sponsons afoul of a barge in such an awkward way that after the application of sledge-hammers and axes had proved unavailing, Captain Harrison ordered the barge to be scuttled. This drastic expedient being promptly accomplished, the ill treated ship at long last escaped and was towed to her moorings off Deptford, followed by a train of small boats and cheering Sunday mariners. Brunel and most of the Company directors and friends were aboard on this first voyage, and the last scene of the first act of a great drama came to a heartfelt close. No task in his eventful engineering career had given Brunel so much anguish, so much euphoria or so much despair, and here at last the victory, certainly a victory over error and misfortune and over the penalties of human vanity. But the burden had been shared—there were several unsung heroes, men who did their duty well; but in Brunel's mind, one suspects, they had done no more than that for which they had been paid. He took very little payment himself. Even so, the fantastic cost of the launch, £170,000, had placed the company about £90,000 in the red and in the necessity of finding something in the region of £120,000 to prepare their ship for the planned voyage to America.

3

THE FITTING OUT

The great ship was in the water but how was she to be completed? About £640,000 had been expended on an unfinished, partially engined and boilered ship which no one seemed to want, with a debt of £90,000 hanging to it like a superfluous anchor. It was not going to be easy to raise the £220,000 recently authorized and retrieve the more recoverable arrears of which the £10,000 owed by a Mr Wythes was not untypical. There was a growing belief among some of the directors that the ship should be put up for sale or auction, and some no doubt saw advantage in organizing its purchase for themselves. Already the use of the ship for conveying an Atlantic cable was being suggested, and Sir Joseph Paxton, a recent director, approached his friends in government to grant a loan or purchase the ship, but without success. *The Times* agreed that the Government could not help the *Great Eastern* without encouraging the kind of irresponsible speculation which it represented. Indeed, it was remarked, this and like experiences had produced a noticeable loss of public confidence in the estimates of promoters. Had the Government acted otherwise, it went on, 'there would be no end to the magnificent works with which projectors would recklessly seek to gain notoriety for themselves at the cost of the community. It may be fine to say that the Thames Tunnel, Great Eastern, and other analogous constructions excite the wonder of foreigners, and should gratify our pride. But there is nothing wonderful in such things except the outlay, since it is an axiom that to engineers there is no impossibility provided there is no limit to the supply of funds.'

The attitude to the *Great Eastern*, as it was now generally called, therefore, was less than warm on the financial market, except perhaps among certain hard-headed financiers who now saw a valuable property coming up for grabs. John Fowler (later Sir John of Forth Bridge fame) was engaged to organize a consortium of contractors to complete the ship since some of the directors were antipathetic to any proposal emanating from Brunel. Realizing this, Brunel made known his readiness to comply with any scheme which would see the work done and not arouse 'party feeling'. When Fowler recommended that John Scott Russell be given an opportunity to submit proposals and estimates for a major part of the contract, Brunel was apprehensive that Russell's sense of grievance might lead him to ask too high a price for the work. Fowler, however, set Russell to work surveying the requirements and Brunel plied Fowler with promptings and advice.

Meantime, the forlorn giant floated patiently, moored fore and aft by pairs of anchors, parallel to the stream of the river. The hazards of this were revealed on 6 April, when furious squalls assailed the ship from a quarter which struck her practically broadside with such effect that the 150 fathom mooring chain on the port bow was strained taut to breaking point. A link about 20ft from the hawse hole suddenly parted, firing off towards the middle of the river as from a cannon, allowing the bow to swing towards the Deptford shore. This placed a further load on the remaining cables in turn such that they all failed one by one within the space of a few minutes, leaving the great hull actually adrift. Fortunately the wind pressed her to the Deptford shore from which she was fended by a barge and a few small vessels, miraculously with little or no damage. Prowse, the chief officer in charge, took all the necessary steps to prevent any further drifting and, one imagines, wiped his brow with relief and telegraphed Captain Harrison to return immediately to help to move his ship safely back on the river.

One afternoon in June, Queen Victoria availed herself of the opportunity to look over the ship with the help of John Yates and Captain Harrison. While being rowed upon the river, Her Majesty, in the words of the chronicler, 'was perforce compelled to hold her bouquet to her face, and the whole party were exceedingly pleased when they reached the shore'. Such was the offensive smell of the Thames in those days. This did not deter the many visitors who paid to see the great wonder, one of whom was moved to complain about the congestion of the narrow access on arrival and the steep shipside ladder which compelled the ladies to make 'a greater display of their charms than was strictly warranted by propriety, and to the extreme amusement of those waiting below'. Similarly positioned was another ladder leading to a lower deck, which not only was very dangerous but gave occasion for 'roars of laughter from groups assembled below' when a lady descended. Another ladder to an office in which prospectuses were dispensed was habitually removed by practical jokers so that people were frequently marooned there, and any person curiously putting his head through a porthole was 'reminded that he was not alone in the vessel by a shower of corks, pieces of biscuit, etc'. This, remarked the perceptive writer, 'did not prepossess one in favour of the new management'.

The requisite financial support of the public was clearly not forthcoming. Investors proved resistant to every blandishment, and there was more than the financial miscalculations which had dogged the *Great Eastern* to blame for this. The years 1857–8 were lean years for shipowners. W.S. Lindsay, recalling this period, wrote that before the close of 1857, markets had become so overstocked with vessels of every kind, that it was hardly possible to obtain remunerative freights for them in any branch of trade.[1] In addition, 1858 saw Far East trade disrupted by the Indian Mutiny, a rising bank rate and several serious bank, as well as mercantile, failures. Nevertheless, exports to the East in 1858 amounted to about a million tons, valued at nearly £54 million. Put like that, it sounded enticing, but not all of it could be attracted to a few sailings of the *Great Eastern* unless there were proper co-ordination of the great ship with feeder connections in the East as originally planned. It was easier said than done. A Mr Griffiths, MP raised the subject of the *Great Eastern* in a speech in the House of Commons, on 9 July 1858, in which he urged the Government to have the Admiralty fit up the ship to lay the transatlantic telegraph cable currently being attempted for the second time—the first was unsuccessful—by two sailing warships approaching each other from opposite sides of the Atlantic. While it was recognized that the *Great Eastern* could accommodate the whole cable, thus avoiding its distribution over two or more lesser craft, the prevailing opinion was that she was too high out of the water for that task and, even more important, the Government saw no way in which to apply funds to assist the operations of a private company, and that was that. But the seed of an idea had been sown which was to bear fruit in time.

Brunel was unconquerable, however, and it was he who obtained the interest of the great railway contractor Thomas Brassey by whose judgement he laid great store.[2] It tipped the balance in the division of opinion existing on the ESN Co board at the time, as to whether to sell or re-finance the ship; Brassey joined with S. Beale,

Jackson, Sir S.M. Peto, MP, E.L. Betts and F. Berkeley, MP, in support of R.J.R. Campbell who wished to act upon a proposal of the city financier L.S. Magnus that they form a new company to which the old company would sell the ship for a modest price. The new company would then raise sufficient capital to complete the ship. The price settled upon was £160,000 and shareholders in the old company were granted the current market value of their shares (£2 10s for a £20 share) towards the purchase of shares in the new. This new company was called the *Great Ship Company* and was incorporated in November 1858 with a capital of £330,000 in £1 shares, to be called up over a period of six months. This left £170,000 of which £140,000 was earmarked for the completion of the ship, after paying off the old company. The prospectus declared that although the best station for the *Great Eastern* was still the Far East, the impetus to traffic and commerce provided by the new Atlantic telegraph 'pointed to the American trade for a more immediate result'. Eight voyages to America per annum at 15 knots, it was estimated, would produce a dividend of 15 per cent. No one could complain about that.

The formation of the new company delayed plans for the completion of the ship and Brunel was ordered by his physician to winter in a warmer climate. He was now, alas, exhibiting the symptoms of the serious kidney ailment which was to cause his untimely death. In January 1859, Russell's proposal and specification for the completion of the ship within six months for a summer voyage to America, for the sum of £125,000 was accepted, and no time was lost in starting the work. The six great masts, five constructed of wrought-iron plate and one wholly of wood, were floated out to the ship on barges and hoisted aboard. Likewise the immense crankshaft, which had been turned and machined on Russell's giant lathe. The delicate task of lifting the shaft from the barge to the ship was entrusted to a floating derrick specially constructed for the task. This was the third and final forging, the first two forgings had to be rejected on account of flaws.

Russell, of course, simply organized and supervised the subcontracting of the many special tasks to established firms—the rigging, the wooden decks, the cabins, the furnishings, the decoration and painting—while his own men fitted the paddle engines and auxiliaries, the Watt Company the screw engines, and Lungley the steering apparatus whereby signals could be transmitted electrically from the bridge to the helmsman at the stern. This was an innovation. The wonder is that so much was accomplished in the circumstances. All supplies had to be delivered by barges, from which they had to be hauled aboard with the help of derricks and tackles. The decks were soon chaotic with timbers, shavings, chains, ropes, pipes, rivet fires, heaps of coke, rolls of carpet, panels and furniture and fittings of every description, all at the mercy of wind and rain and frequent streams of incredibly inquisitive spectators, who provided a revenue which the directors were reluctant to forego. Nevertheless they did so, however, for some weeks in July and August while Russell was pushing the work to a close. Over all hung the nauseating stench of the polluted river which made some of even the least sensitive workers feel sick. By the end of July the paddle engines had been given a gentle whirl and deemed ready. To mark the virtual completion of his contract, Russell held a banquet on board on the evening of 8 August, attended by Members of Parliament, directors of the Company and by professional people interested in the enterprise. Brunel was unable to attend, but, since his return from Egypt in May, he had been almost daily aboard the ship in his capacity of Company engineer. Alas, he was far from well and now a tragic wreck of the tough, energetic little giant, who had dominated every scene he had entered.

Trouble, again brewing on the financial front, came to the surface at a shareholders' meeting on 21 August, at which the board asked authority to issue the 30,000 shares they had reserved to send the *Great Eastern* on her first voyage. One faction supported the efforts of J.O. Lever to charter the ship, but Lever's first offer of £30,000 was rejected by the board and a move to have his second offer read to the meeting was defeated. L.S. Magnus, who was disgruntled and who made himself very troublesome, angrily disputed the necessity for any further increase in capital and particularly the intention not to insure the ship, which may suggest the nature of his financial interests. He alleged that several advantageous contracts had been declined and that several charges he had made against the board had been ignored. When his amendment to appoint a committee of inquiry was defeated, he embarked upon a campaign to step up his harassment of the management to get his way.

It was resolved to move the ship from the Thames to Weymouth early in September, then run a trial trip out into the Atlantic, to be followed shortly thereafter by a maiden voyage to Portland, Maine, with passengers and freight. Between 150 and 200 first-class passengers at £6 and £10 according to cabin, were accepted for the trip to Weymouth, along with a number of newspaper correspondents and honoured guests. The departure was postponed from 30 August to 6 September, the passengers boarding the ship on the eve of departure. On 5 September, after observing a test of the paddle engines, Brunel suffered a slight stroke and had to be carried home.

A further twenty-four hours were required to complete essential work but much clearing up, decorating, finishing and attaching remained to be done as the day of departure dawned. This remains a not unusual experience with new ships in general; but the *Great Eastern* presented a peculiarly chaotic spectacle to those coming aboard at the last moment. One had to be very tired to sleep through the strange hammerings, clangings, thumps and voices of the night. Then steam was raised and the engines warmed up, so that by seven o'clock the patient monster was ready to move out of its birthplace. Captain Harrison, accompanied by Mr Atkinson, the chief pilot, and Scott Russell, who transmitted the requisite signals to the engine rooms, mounted the bridge, and with a temporary crew of Messrs Westhorp's riggers and the help of several volunteers including the visiting Captain Comstock of the American Collins Line, took their stations. The six mooring chains were slipped with an ear-splitting roar, ribbons of flame flashing from the hawse holes, and with six tugs in attendance she headed down river to the wonder of the multitude.

The iron monster, so long an inert and fantastic presence in the river, was seen actually to be moving under her own power in pace with her escorts. A fleet of steamers pursued her out of the fog from Westminster and shoals of little boats scrambled out from various berths on the river to enliven the procession. Word quickly spread, and soon hundreds of people assembled at every vantage point along the way, cheering and waving, while the pilot with Russell at the engine telegraph, anxiously steered the monster round the difficult bends. The combination of paddles and screw gave the ship remarkable manoeuvrability. One particular trick was to turn her practically about her own axis while at a halt by putting the rudder hard over while the paddles were put in reverse against the forward thrust of the screw, the stream from the screw impinging on the rudder to give the stern a sideways movement. Her first anxiety arose from a barque anchored in the navigating channel near Blackwall. This she

Richard Tangye beside one of the Tangye hydraulic rams used during launching operations in December 1857 (*Brunel University Library*)

A group of directors inspecting the launch preparations. On the right is the aft brake drum and the levers which tightened the brake bands on the rims of the drum. At the top of the picture, between the paddle-wheel and the access tower, may be seen the projecting platform from which Brunel planned to direct the operation of fore and aft brakes. The chains running down the ship's side from the paddle sponson were connected to winches aboard barges in the river (*Smithsonian Institution*)

The crankshaft being hoisted aboard during fitting out (*Illustrated London News*)

The *Great Eastern* with her escort of tugs on her way down river in September 1859 (*Illustrated London News*)

avoided only by moving dangerously near the limit of the deep water. For a moment it was thought she was aground, but vigorous backing of paddles and screw and a sideways pull by the tugs swung her clear. She took the short bend at Greenwich by backing out a little and canting round, and three hours from departure arrived off Woolwich, a distance of fourteen miles, having navigated all hazards to everyone's relief and satisfaction. Some few lesser ones remained, and the ship was therefore anchored off Purfleet for the night to await the favourable tide of the morning. Numerous guests came aboard, including the Marquis of Stafford and Lord Alfred Paget, some journalists and some unauthorized persons who smuggled themselves on in various ways.

Scores of sightseers sailed round the ship in a series of excursion steamers and pleasure craft, while bands played patriotic airs and passing ships turned out on deck and in the rigging to cheer and dip their flags. It was a great commotion on and off the water, and when at low tide the great ship swung round and blocked off all traffic in the moonlight, no one took exception.

The correspondent for Charles Dickens' *Household Words*[3] found it impossible to sleep 'within hearing of the siege of Sebastopol, the workshops of a hundred active Tubal Caine's, the barking roar of some great steam monster puffing up a pipe as broad as a main sewer, the ceaseless blows of a steam water-pumping engine, and the fretful tapping of an iron chain against the iron casing of the vessel. It was not necessary to add the barking of a dog to this, except to fill up the intervals between the louder noises.' Of the pilot coming aboard he commented that he could never understand why pilots should attend to work a vessel in opera costume. As the great ship's procession continued past Gravesend to the Nore, the same tumult of public enthusiasm greeted it at every stage. 'The whole county of Kent', he continued, 'seemed to be assembled in piers and gardens to watch our progress. The people looking like beds of flowers as they sat motionless on the land; and the ships in the river were bending down with the human fruit on their decks and in their rigging.'[3]

As the dirty black water of the river gave way to the sea, the boilers, taking sea water, began to prime—that is to foam and carry over slugs of water to the engines—and as A.L. Holley, a noted American engineer, observed, threw showers of muddy water from the steam pipes all over the deck. This soon stopped, however, and about the same time the tugs were released to the ceremonial playing of the national anthem by the band. The *Great Eastern* took off grandly, on her very own at last, heading for the Nore light in the vicinity of which she anchored for the night.

The dinner speeches of the day were, thought A.L. Holley, in keeping with the general management of the enterprise: 'Mr Brunel who did not *originate* the ship was glorified, and Mr Scott Russell whose sense and energy were almost the parent of the actual ship was rather slighted. But Mr Russell's speech—he was at last called up for decency's sake—was modest and instructive. He traced the history of large vessels, and ascribed the credit to the proper parties, especially to Charles Wood of Glasgow, who, he said, had done more than any other Englishman in the cause of improved ocean navigation. He also acknowledged the merits of the Americans in this department. I am glad to say, incidentally, that Mr Russell will spend some time in the States after the passage of the *Great Eastern*.'[4] What Holley means by the word 'originate' is not clear. He must have heard Russell himself say that the 'original conception' of the ship was due to Brunel and been aware of Brunel's specific contributions to the structural design, to which Russell also testified. It is evident that Holley was not ready to jump on the bandwagon of unreserved adulation of the great engineer and in this he was not alone, although he may have been in the minority. He was of that party which took the view that Brunel had 'caused untold loss to the Company', and of that group of engineers and shipbuilders who sympathized with Russell as a victim of the appetites of the project and perhaps of Brunel. But it was a peculiarly poignant moment. Brunel, an engineer of immense accomplishment, a giant in his profession, had burned himself out with years of action-crammed days and nights with only a few hours ever devoted to sleep, and that often in a half-upright position in his easy chair in his special personal railway car. Now, his last great conception and the subject of immense anxieties and toil was being led to fulfilment in his enforced absence. He had earlier been hauled like a wounded hero on a litter, across the recently completed Saltash Bridge, but, felled by nephritis and a stroke, he was now far too ill to be moved. It was natural in these circumstances especially that compassionate men's thoughts should be impelled with a desire to honour the mainspring of the work with which they were so intimately associated.

Things were going very well with the ship; everyone was pleased with her. The great paddle engines, especially, commanded much admiration and her easy motion and responses gave the lie to those who had predicted her too large and clumsy for safety. Certainly none on board had ever been aboard anything bigger than a ship less than half the size. It was a dramatic experience to be on a floating multi-storey hotel and observe from its steady heights the heavings and dippings of lesser craft which reminded one of how it had normally felt to travel on these seas. One troublesome and somewhat ominous weakness was steering power. Even in the easy seas off the channel coast, at least four men hauled on the helms, sometimes aided with a steam winch, and the system was designed for about ten helmsmen.

There was inordinate interest in the crucial question of the ship's speed and the respective contributions of paddles and screw and whether the one interfered with the other. Naval men, engineers and financiers alike took out their watches and timed the revolutions of screw and paddle wheels and timed the passage of objects in the water, then extrapolated, from a knowledge of the boilers in operation and the steam pressure, the speed which might reasonably be expected under ideal conditions with the ship in proper trim. There was, of course, precious little for these knowledgeable observers to do and the newspaper correspondents had to make copy of all their chatter.

It was not generally realized that the ship was not yet on trial. The engine builders were still in control of the usage and speed of their engines and were determined not to force them. Some bearings on the screw engines were giving trouble and some of the donkey engines driving the boiler feed pumps were unable to deliver whenever the boiler pressure exceeded about 18psi. There were no sight glasses on the boilers of those days, the level of the boiler water being ascertained by the regular opening of three suitably placed cocks. No amount of adjustment of the feed pump relief valves seemed to improve the situation. The engine room staffs were officially members of the crew, sailing under ship's orders, the senior men being former employees of the respective engine builders. Russell's former engine works manager, John Dickson, although not a member of the crew, kept a watchful eye over his great engine; its speed and that of the screw engine being reported to Russell at intervals.

One fearsome danger was overlooked or underestimated in the preoccupation with so many distractions. The two forward funnels serving the paddle boilers were encased for a length of about forty feet by a feed-water jacket through which the feed-water passed on its way to the boilers. These jackets served two purposes—to utilize some of the flue gas heat otherwise rejected and to insulate the saloons through which the funnels passed. To each jacket was attached a standpipe which, after projecting upwards alongside the funnel, bent over on itself back down into the stokehold. At the bend was drilled a ½in hole which served as a vent to break any syphon effect and possibly serve as a safety valve in the event of the feed-water's being cut off from the jacket and the jacket contents being converted into steam. The danger here was that, should water be introduced to the jackets after they had boiled dry, there could poss-ibly be a rapid generation of steam and a resultant explosion. The funnel would have very much less resistance to buckling under excessive pressure than would its outer jacket to rupture, hence the need to stay the inner surface especially. There was no staying of the *Great Eastern*'s two funnel heaters. Both Russell and the Watt Co had objected to the heaters, but while Brunel was in sole charge of the construction he had them fitted to the paddle boiler flues. He had used a similar heater on the *Great Britain* with no accidents, but other applications had not been so fortunate.

The principle of striving for maximum economy of the heat of combustion was sound but the particular means of accomplishing this by way of the funnel jackets on the *Great Eastern* was not. However, the arrangement was made peculiarly lethal by the pres-ence of cocks at the bottom of the standpipes and by their being closed at a time when the feed-water was by-passed directly to the boilers. The evil consequences of this might have been avoided if the communications from the jackets to the boilers had been open; but it would appear from what happened that this was not the case.

The hair-raising aspect of this is that these veritable time bombs passed through the main saloon which was often full of passengers. Dickens' correspondent rather cynically described the main saloon as the Italian Court of the ship, 'a gilded sham ... It had nothing like sea-going comfort about it. Its space was limited for so large a ship, and its many mirrors were engaged all day and night in deluding the passengers as to the extent of their chief sitting room. The couches are placed round those two highly decorated and beglazed funnel shafts, which stood at each end of this Italian Court upon the water, a couple of smiling volcanoes. As you looked in those glittering mirrors, to adjust your cravat, or brush back your flowing hair, you might have seen the dim outline of a death's head peering over your shoulder. Behind their deceitful faces was a steaming mass of destructive water, ready to explode at any moment.'[5]

It was, of course, in ignorance of this that the banquet was held in the main saloon at the Nore, and that people gathered there after dinner, late in the afternoon of the day on which the ship left the Nore on its way to Weymouth. The tranquillity and ease of the ship gave rise to all the greater shock when, just off Hastings at about six o'clock in the evening, the feed-water jacket on the forward funnel exploded, launching the funnel like a rocket into the air amid a shower of debris and billowing smoke. The scene in the stokehold was horrifying. The furnaces blew back and scalding water from the ruptured heater and much wreckage was showered over the boilers and stokers on the floor. There was an immediate danger of fire, especially with the unkempt array of combustibles around.

On deck, men wildly rushed about, some trying to lower boats and others creating further panic by exclaiming that the ship was sinking and that the other boilers would go at any moment. Holley, indeed, thought a boiler had burst and looked anxiously at the level of the ship in the water, while an old carpenter sawing off a plank at the stern of the ship halted with his knee still on the wood then resumed sawing once the debris had settled. The main saloon was a shambles but fortunately it had been empty and only two people, one of whom being Captain Harrison's young daughter, had been in the cabins leading off it. They were unscathed, but not so the poor stokers. Russell and some others descended into the *mêlée*, he ordered the fires to be drawn while members of the crew rescued their stricken comrades, some terribly scalded or burned. One had jumped out of an ash chute and had held on to a beam of the paddle box for a time before falling into the churning wake of the paddles while the rest were painfully escorted or carried aft to what was called the dispensary.

This, however, had been used as a carpenters' shop was was littered with shavings and wood. Mattresses were hastily procured and the casualties were led, according to a witness, 'down a dark and double flight of steps, by the light of a flickering candle, round a corner, and between two long tables, across a lower unfinished common dining saloon, through another rough deal door, and down a dark winding staircase; across a kind of hold, up a pair of ladder steps, and along two passages.... It was a low-roofed, dirty, wretched place, with a small surgery at the end, and as one man was putting down mattresses, and preparing blanket-beds, another was sweeping up the shavings, dirt, and chips from the floor... A number of beds were pulled to pieces for the sake of the white soft wool they contained, and when the half-boiled bodies of the poor creatures were anointed with oil, they were covered over with this wool, and made to lie down. They were nearly all stokers and firemen, whose faces were black with their work, and one man, who was brought in had patches of red raw flesh on his dark, agonized face, like dabs of red paint, and the skin of his arms was hanging from his hands like a pair of tattered mittens. He was marked early for peace and death, while the others ... were moaning, and complaining of thirst or cold.' They were attended by the two ship's doctors and a doctor from among the passengers. Three of the dozen injured died during the night and another died later.[6]

Captain Harrison steered the ship towards the shore until it could be ascertained that she was neither holed nor about to blow up. Immediately after the explosion, one of the engineers on the engine platform, with commendable intelligence, hastened to check the stopcock on the standpipe of the remaining heater and, finding it shut, opened it, effecting a great effusion of steam from the vent and the avoidance of another explosion. A hose was played upon the burning debris and furnaces of the affected boiler, and somehow order was restored leaving everyone much shaken and subdued. The management of the Company tried to persuade the newspaper men on board to play down the accident 'to ensure the commercial success of the undertaking', and, of course, no word of it escaped from the ship until she arrived at Weymouth about ten the next morning. The cheers from the welcoming fleet of pleasure-boats and yachts died away when the ship's colours were seen to be flying half mast and the demeanour of the *Great Eastern*'s passengers appeared so curiously restrained. Some would also note with dismay the absence of a funnel.

The Company held Russell responsible for the repair of the damage resulting from the heater explosion and for the 'engineering neglect', as they termed it, which was alleged to have caused it. Russell countered that his responsibility did not include the control of the actual operation of the power plant, that this was the duty of the ship's engineers, serving as they were under ship's articles. The help he and Dickson afforded was voluntary and, Russell declared, motivated by a desire to help. If the voyage from the Thames to Weymouth could be called a trial trip, it was not his, Russell's, trial trip. If the heater's failure was due to its design, and it could have been, then he certainly could not be held responsible, since it had not been designed under his direction. He was not recorded as extending his denial of responsibility to the engines and boilers manufactured under his charge. That he felt in some measure responsible for the engines and boilers obliged him, presumably, to supervise their treatment. The engines were not to be forced or incorrectly used, and he and Dickson were there to see to it; likewise, the Watt representatives were concerned with the care of their engines. Much of the construction of the ship had been carried out under the Company's responsibility. The presence and design of the heater were due to Brunel and, according to Dickson, he had not objected to the retention of the mischievous stopcocks. The ship was under the command of Captain Harrison, aided by several people, such as Captain Comstock, who were volunteering their professional assistance. It was all very casual.

Testimony given at the inquest into the death of the five unfortunate stokers established that the cocks on the heater standpipes were open when the ship left the Thames, but that no one had given the order to close the cocks although they were closed at the time of the explosion. The explosion was attributed to the closing of these cocks coupled with the discontinuance of the flow of feed-water through the heaters to the boilers. If, indeed, the cocks were open when the ship left Deptford, the most likely occasion for closing them would occur when the ship first drew sea water and muddy water was flicked over the deck from what were called the 'steam pipes' on the funnels. The inquest could not establish responsibility but held the engineers of the paddle engines in some measure negligent. It was all regretfully typical of the tale of the great ship, as indeed was the tragic news of Brunel's death at the age of fifty-three on 15 September, midway through the inquest.

Russell directed the repair of the explosion damage, estimated at £5,000, but the finances of the Company were again embarrassed, and whether for this or some more subtle reason, some of the directors lost enthusiasm for the trip to America. They eagerly grasped the delay and bad publicity occasioned by the accident as a convenient excuse to counsel postponement. Others were anxious to adhere to the original plan when the repairs were completed in three weeks, and the ship left its train loads of trippers at Weymouth and proceeded on a two-day trial trip to Holyhead. The trial trip passed off well, the ship established her easiness, particularly in a heavy head sea, and while the data were not made available, it was evident to the *cognoscenti* that while she would not be nearly as fast as some had anticipated, she was capable of maintaining 14 knots with the steam available. The engines, particularly the great paddle engines, were acknowledged marvels of mechanical engineering and it was established that she could do the job for which she was designed. This, however, was not to work the Atlantic trade.

But there were a number of items, including Board of Trade requirements, which would have to be attended to before she could enter service, and the directors had arranged with the London & North Western Railway Co—in which some of them also had an interest—to run excursions to Holyhead from the Midlands. The voyage to America became increasingly unlikely and, not surprisingly, some of the shareholders wanted to know what the directors were about. The directors had turned down J.O. Lever's second bid to charter the ship, reputedly for £40,000 per annum, on the grounds of lack of confidence in his establishing the good repute of the ship, and had tried to persuade the Government to take it over or subsidize it. This was alluded to by Gladstone, the Chancellor of the Exchequer, and other members of the Government, on the occasion of a grand banquet held by the London & Northern Western Railway Co in a pavilion in the grounds of the Royal Hotel, Holyhead, on the evening of 20 October. Gladstone poured cold water on their hopes yet again—the Government had no place in the board rooms of the nation.

When the guests departed, snow covered the Welsh hills and the chilly sea seemed all the more inhospitable to a ship which was too large to enjoy the protection of the breakwater of the harbour, and a great storm on 24–25 October, emphasized the unsuitability of Holyhead for her winter anchorage. In this storm the breakwater was partially destroyed and many of the vessels cowering in its shelter were swept aground or sunk. The steamship *Royal Charter*, within hours of home after a long voyage from Australia, was tragically lost nearby with few survivors, while the *Great Eastern* battled against the gale with many anxious moments in the pitch darkness. By eight o'clock in the evening of the first day, it was evident that she could not comfortably depend upon her two anchors. Captain Harrison therefore ordered steam up and kept a close lookout for any drift. By the early hours of the morning, the rain, hail and spume were sweeping all before them. When the Captain struggled to the bow, hoping to pierce the thick gloom ahead, he had to beat an undignified retreat with his waterproof coat blown to ribbons, and ended up in a heap, bowled over on the deck. The saloon skylights flapped up and down and broke one after the other, exposing the saloon to the rain and spray.

By the next evening, the harbour was strewn with timber from the breakwater, while an eerie luminosity suffused the waves, reflecting a whitish glare from the clouds above. To ease the strain upon the anchors, the screw was started cautiously but it was fouled by the floating timbers and the paddles had to be risked to lend a hand. One anchor was raised preparatory to moving to a better location but the load falling upon the remaining cable increased to breaking point, as the ship swung off into a beam sea, and parted with a startling recoil. Unsecured, the great ship reeled drunkenly towards the shore. The free anchor was quickly let go, but such was the ship's momentum that this was hopelessly inadequate. The screw, however, gradually drove her towards her anchor and had almost attained mastery when a large mass of wreckage fouled it. Again resort was made to the paddles, desperately driven this time at speed and regardless of damage, until the screw could be freed. At last the anchor held and the ship settled to a more comfortable riding position, but not before she had tugged and rolled upon her chain, some of the links of which were permanently stretched. This phenomenal gale left a trail of horror and destruction on land and sea, including the heart-rending loss of the *Royal Charter*. It was of some account, therefore, that the great ship in the heart of the storm should have survived with such apparent ease, although it was a close run thing as those on the bridge well knew.

The weather was now too cold and wet for tourists and the Holyhead boarding houses and hotels which so recently had been turning away visitors in droves now found business as usual for the time of year. It was announced that the *Great Eastern* would move to Southampton where she could winter more safely and draw upon a new public of sightseers, although no one said as much. When she steamed out of Holyhead, the citizens ignored the event and left it to a group of railway officials on a steam tug to bid her a grateful farewell. It would have been no less appropriate for a like delegation from the London & South Western Railway Co to have met the ship on her arrival at Southampton.

Despite a visit by the Prince Consort and despite the banqueting and cajoling, the Government remained indifferent to all entreaties to subsidize the great ship. The directors were now in trouble and they had to face the music of their shareholders, a music which was becoming increasingly audible and discordant, with no ameliorating compensations to offer. Some of them fed the newspapers with details of the work which would have to be done to the ship, or which they thought would have to be done, before she could brave the Atlantic and, if anything, exaggerated the difficulties. Unfortunately, while they hoped by this means to shift the responsibility on to the contractor, they also gave ammunition to those disaffected shareholders and board members who, led by Magnus, sought to destroy the directorate. The unpalatable fact was that there was insufficient capital to send the ship to America and the managing directors were afraid to admit it. About £27,000 of shares remained to be issued, but the current market value of the *Great Eastern* shares was only about one-fifth of their face value. It was represented that Russell had not completed his contract satisfactorily, and that consequently the directors had withheld his final payment of £6,000. In accordance with the terms of their contract, the directors and Russell submitted their dispute to three arbitrators; one selected by each party and a third by the arbitrators themselves. The men chosen were John Hawkshaw, John Fowler and J.R. McClean, all very distinguished civil engineers, who appear in turn to have called upon Mundella, Field and Penn to help them in their task.

To help destroy the management, although at the risk of also destroying whatever remained of public confidence in the undertaking, Magnus' faction commissioned three eminent shipwrights to survey the ship at Holyhead and report upon her deficiencies. The surveyors reported back on 18 October, and towards the end of November their critical remarks were leaked to the press to the further embarrassment of the Company, upon which Campbell was quick to tell *The Times*' financial editor that he intended to request the shareholders to appoint a committee to investigate the affairs of the Company. Thus he stole a march on his critics, particularly on Magnus, who had been pushing for such an inquiry since August. There was no escaping the fact that a million pounds had been expended on a ship which was not expected to have cost half as much and which was represented as not yet ready to enter service. Magnus' surveyors, George Bayley, William Patterson and John Jordan, listed a host of minor deficiencies which one imagines were of a kind which could have been listed for almost any sizable new ship. The insufficient combings and gratings on skylights may have been more significant, as also the need for a tunnel to enclose the screw shaft and more secure 'watercloset stools' in some parts. The planking on the main deck was inferior and there was no doubt it leaked at the seams; but this was only what Russell called a carpet over an iron deck. Nor does one feel so confident of their opinion that some of the beams in the cargo spaces should have been supported by pillars. Russell and Brunel knew something of the strength of iron beams.

Just what was legitimately chargeable to Russell is impossibe for us to know, nor do we know what adjustment was made for the inferior deck planking by Russell's subcontractor. The arbitrators had all this to consider. Such items as the need for improved ventilation of the stokeholds, and the feed pump problems, were revealed by the trial trips. The Board of Trade, too, required some modifications or additions to meet safety regulations. Whatever the significance of these considerations, the newspaper correspondents passed on their own judgements and those of others as their own, and nothing was too trivial for their notice. One cannot imagine any similar engineering enterprise today receiving the same detailed attention or the modern reading public finding patience for the pros and cons of nuts and bolts which, apparently, the newspaper readers of the 1850s found of absorbing interest. The laws of libel, too, were clearly easier then. At last, on 10 December, the Company announced that it had entered into some financial arrangement to relieve them of the pressure of current liabilities amounting to about £45,000. Some irate shareholders called a meeting at which they let off much steam, accusing the management of wheeling and dealing with the contractors and of profligate expenditure—£20,000 on wines and £10,000 on coals and so on. The directorate, under siege, tore itself apart with mutual betrayal in the shadow of valueless shares and a monster ship they could not manage.

Some insight into the character of the strife was given by A.L. Holley who wrote:

The fact is that Messrs Campbell and Jackson, MP, (a quondam trader on the Gold Coast of by no means brilliant antecedents) had everything their own way, until the bursting of the heater or funnel casement... Then Magnus, who had always protested against all their acts, but who had been completely extinguished by them, came into active opposition on the strength of the accident. Mr Jackson who had called Mr Magnus a liar at a previous meeting, having split with Campbell, owing to a quarrel, it is said, about an anticipated knighthood which was not conferred upon either, now sides with Magnus, and magnanimously wishes to resign to make way for Magnus and Bold, the latter being a nominee of his own. Then one Guedella, of the Stock Exchange, calls a meeting of his own, and abuses everything that has been done. Him the valiant Magnus threatens and dares to single combat, and the matter was... brought before the Lord Mayor by means of a summons obtained by the timorous Guedella who was big enough to annihilate Magnus had he so dared.[14]

Fireworks were predicted for the general meeting of the Company, now called for early in January, and none of the directors could have been looking forward to it.

4

BREAKING FREE

A very determined and disgruntled congregation of shareholders and directors packed themselves into a room in the London Tavern on 11 January 1860, to do battle with whoever or whatever had robbed them of their rest throughout the past few months. R.J.R. Campbell, the chairman, with his back to the wall in face of six notices of motion for the creation of committees of inquiry and a new board, was ready to capitulate; Magnus with his faction supported by Jackson MP, his newfound ally of convenience who had defected from the board, was ready to take possession; William Hawes, with most of the board's support, was ready to accept Lever's offer to charter and the consideration of any offer of purchase, and several groups of enraged shareholders conspicuous among whom being the Rev Mr Nicholson, a florid, red-haired parson with five or six thousand depreciated shares to avenge and armed with a potent vocabulary of abuse to hurl at his persecutors, were ready for a fracas.

The secretary, John Yates, had not long proceeded to read the notices of motion when he was interrupted by loud cries for a larger room, whereupon the business was halted until the irate throng could jostle its way into the largest room in the house. Order being restored, the secretary, doggedly competent, read out the directors' report. The incendiary nature of the agenda was doused in anticipation by the announcement of the board's resignation—loud cheers. The bad news, however, included the report that the ship had been mortgaged for £40,000 at 7½ per cent for six months, which left a deficit of £36,641 after an expenditure of £353,957.

William Hawes' proposal of a committee to report, in the first instance, on the sale or charter of the ship, then to inquire into the past management and future prospects of the Company, raised several questions which aroused suspicions of preconcert among the shareholders. One uproar followed another with the exchange of threats and bad language, culminating in the Rev Mr Nicholson and Mr Abel and some others indulging in a free exchange of personalities, apparently to the satisfaction and amusement of all except a few who thought the turning of the meeting into a bear garden could jeopardize their property.

'This affair', wrote Holley for the *New York Times*, 'is not likely to increase the popularity of limited liability companies. What with salaries and commissions, banquets and jobbing, patronage and facilities for bulling and bearing the stock; what with scrambling and abuse, recrimination and jealousy, the interests of the shareholders go to the wall.'

When Hawes' amendment was defeated by a show of hands, he demanded a poll, whereupon the meeting was adjourned for a week so that a poll could be conducted. The poll confirmed the rejection, and a much reduced and less vituperative meeting ultimately elected a committee of inquiry differing in composition from that proposed by Hawes and including the Rev Mr Nicholson.[1] They would look into such matters as the contract with Scott Russell, and why the ship sailed to Weymouth and Holyhead. The answer to the latter was, of course, well known.

Meantime, Scott Russell called for a return to sanity and purpose in a statement printed on gilt-edged paper which he circulated to all the shareholders. In this he emphasized the excellent seagoing qualities and manoeuvrability of the great ship as now amply proved; that she was the strongest vessel in the world and, with her system of watertight bulkheads, one of the safest. Her speed, he asserted, was almost exactly that assigned by Mr Brunel, and no one, he argued, had a right to expect more from her extremely small proportion of power for her size of which the object was primarily great economy of fuel on a long voyage, a voyage of over 13,000 miles. Certainly the Company owed him money for work done, but he wanted no more than those 'honest and able arbitrators', to whom they had both referred the matter, should apportion him. They were not enemies, he shared their interest in the great ship and indeed he was one of the largest shareholders. 'If you can agree', he sagely concluded, 'upon men of ability, experience, and success in the management of steam property, to take the entire practical control of the executive part of your business, you will not be disappointed with the result.' In offering this wise advice, Russell no doubt had one eye on the exemplary precedent of the Cunard Co.

Russell's advice did not go unheeded, but the conflicts of self interest among the directors seeking control, some of whom had unexpressed plans of their own, made it irrelevant. The committee of investigation, through its chairman Samuel Baker, reported after a time that since they had difficulty in obtaining the necessary information they did not feel warranted in passing a judgement, one way or the other, on the previous management. They found it necessary to express the opinion that Magnus' actions were influenced by a conscientious desire to forward the interests of the Company. They recommended a new Board comprising the Marquis of Stafford, Captain C.E. Mangles, Mr H.T. Hope, Mr S Baker, the Hon Capt Carnegie RN, Mr J.R. Croskey and Mr Daniel Gooch. Certainly this included some 'practical' men but, unlike Cunard, MacIvor and Burns of the Cunard Line, none had managed a line of steamships. But they were given support to the extent of being authorized to increase the nominal capital of the Company by £100,000 to £430,000 and to send the ship on a voyage to America. A survey of the work required to meet Board of Trade requirements and supply certain deficiencies of accommodation and machinery revealed that the whole could be met by a sum of about £20,000; much less than the public had been led to expect. Included in this was the fitting of steam blast pipes to the funnels to improve the draft and ventilation. Messrs Lungley, and Penn and Field, executed the contracts.

The bizarre hand of fate again grasped the *Great Eastern* on the morning of the 21 January 1860. Her excellent captain, so long prepared for his great duty, set out from Hythe for Southampton in one of the ship's boats, called a gig. Captain Harrison was at the helm in the stern while Dr Watson, the ship's surgeon, Captain Lay, superintendent purser, and his son of nine years of age, the coxswain and five of the crew, arranged themselves to balance the heel. The wind became squally near the docks and the water choppy and broken, and as the gig cleaved her foamy way into this, Captain Harrison gave orders to stand by with the halyards. When he ordered down sail to enter the docks, the halyards and sail, being soaked, stuck part way and caught a contrary gust from the dock opening which jibed the sail. The boat heeled over on the loaded side and capsized. The occupants were thrown into the cold, grey water and stifling spray. Captain Harrison struck out for the upturned boat and tried unsuccessfully to right it, but, becoming exhausted by these exertions and the cold, could only hold on weakly with the help of Dr Watson who had already caught hold of the boy between himself and the upturned boat. The captain, unfortunately, fell away, to be picked up unconscious by one of the rescuers from the nearby ships and docks. He did not recover despite much effort during an hour and a half which included the application of a galvanic battery. Young Lay and Ogden, the coxswain, were also drowned, but the remainder were saved.

Captain Harrison could not easily be replaced; but in Captain John Vine Hall, a well-experienced steamship commander in the Eastern trade, he had a successor of some standing who had been commander of one of the ships on which Brunel had travelled to or from Egypt. Brunel had been much struck on one occasion by the originality of Captain Hall's contrivance for repairing his ship in the absence of a dock. It was under this new commander that the *Great Eastern* was prepared and tuned for her maiden voyage to New York on 16 June. The plan to make Portland, Maine, the port of call was abandoned, and the repeated on again off again statements and rumours as to the departure date did little for her bookings. People, too, had become afraid of her—she was jinxed. Hence only 38 passengers, and 8 guests, embarked, although accommodation was provided for 300.[2] Even the *Great Britain* had more passengers on her maiden voyage. The New York papers made much of the misfortunes of the great ship and now expressed doubts that this, the latest offspring of British arrogance and muddle would ever be seen in America. At last the intelligence from Europe seemed to confirm that the great ship was really about to set out and, if so, it could be expected to arrive any day after the 25th of the month. In fact, her departure was actually delayed a day on account of the drunkenness of the crew, a circumstance which Daniel Gooch deplored as indicative of a lack of discipline.

When there was still no sign of her on the 27th, the *New York Times* prepared its readers for another fiasco, but before going to press on the morning of the 28th, a message was received from Sandy Hook telegraph station that the lights of a large vessel were visible in the vicinity of the lightship. It was believed that this must be the *Great Eastern*, and so indeed it proved to be. It was noted with disappointment that the voyage had taken 10 days 19 hours, and Gooch disapproved of the fact that the captain had been more intent in giving his small coterie of passengers a pleasant trip by dipping too far south into the Gulf Stream than in taking the shortest route. But

An engraving of the *Great Eastern* published in 1859 by William Foster of Fenchurch Street, showing her fully rigged (*Science Museum*)

This photograph is thought to have been taken at Milford Haven after one of the cable laying trips (*Peabody Museum of Salem*)

The Grand Saloon. Note the square funnel casings lined by mirrors (*Illustrated London News*)

A family saloon cabin (*Illustrated London News*)

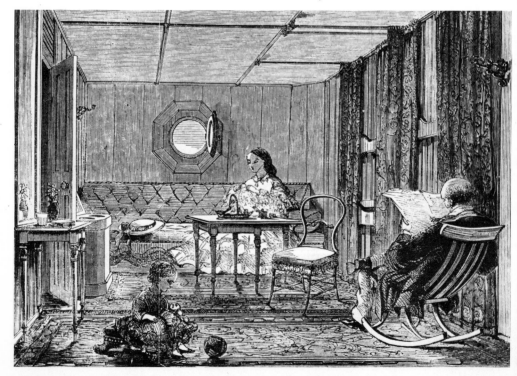

the passengers had indeed enjoyed the voyage and the comments of one of these, George Wilkes, editor of *Wilkes' Spirit of the Times*, give us a concise impression of the trip and an idea of all in the experience that was novel to a seasoned transatlantic traveller:

Monday, June 18. I was awoke this morning by the sun shining brightly through my port-hole (I should rather use the plural, for my sumptuous apartment was lit by two), and I rose to enjoy the luxury of dressing in a carpeted space as large almost as a room in the St Nicholas. Before I got up, however I lay for a few minutes to observe the silence and quiet of the vessel. In fact, there seemed to be no motion to her at all, and had it not been for the barely perceptible buzz of her bow—to which I was very near—as it split the water and passed it humming along the vessel's beautiful wave-line, I should not have been able to decide with certainty whether she was going on or standing still. Vibration there was none, and as for the usual clatter of machinery, which is the distinguishing feature of a steamship, it could not be heard at all. Moreover, there was not any of the squeaking and squealing of timbers and tortured wood work, which makes up a hideous serenade on all other vessels, for our party-walls, our state-room floors and ceilings, are of iron, and so ribbed and morticed, and joined stiffly with the hull, that the ship, while passing through still water, seems to be one solid tube or beam. Indeed, I could not make it certain to my senses that she had not stopped, until, looking out of my port-hole, I saw the ocean passing by, and our vast mass moving gradually through it like a floating castle. When I went on deck I found the air cool and bracing, but all there was of wind was caused by our own motion. At eight o'clock her paddle-engines gave ten revolutions, and those for the propeller twenty-nine, while the log, which was heaved a few minutes afterwards, credited her with a rate of ten knots. After timing the stroke of the engines I took a look at the rapidly-revolving paddles, and found that their original diameter of fifty-six feet, which had proved to be too large, had been reduced to fifty feet by reefing or drawing in the floats, or paddles, three feet on each arm. A large projection of useless iron consequently extends beyond the actual wheels to make an unnecessary resistance to the water, and I am told that the wheel would do better still if the floats were reefed in yet farther.

I now took my first promenade around the deck, and though well instructed in its vast proportions, I could not help wondering, as I went on, to see the space unroll before me as it did. Standing at the stern and looking forward, the vessel seems almost to terminate amid-ships, but when you reach that point there appears to open up another ship before you. This illusion proceeds from the fact that two large life-boats, which had hung outside towards the bow, had been brought in at the request of the Board of Trade, and set on blocks in the centre of the ship to divide the view. These, however, will be removed as soon as the vessel gets into port, and then there will be restored a clean, unobstructed double avenue, through which our friend Hiram Woodruff might drive a double team, and go only four times

77

round to make a mile. The deck is flush from stem to stern, and its only obstructions are the six masts, the five smoke-funnels in between, the raised skylights for cabin ventilation, and seven low structures, all of which run in a line with the masts and smoke-stacks. The two outermost of these—stem and stern—are sheds for the donkey or auxiliary engines; two are erections for the main cabin entrances; one spacious one in the centre of the quarter-deck is allotted to the captain; another of like character is the double residence of the first and second officers, and another still, of tolerable size, is given to the passengers as a smoking-room. These are the only obstructions which are found on deck, while around them runs a clean twelve-foot promenade, one side of which has been named Broadway and the other Fifth Avenue. The floor of the deck, like the hull of the ship, is of iron, and built like the sides, on the tubular principle, with twenty-one inches of space between its walls, and interlaced and strapped, crossed and recrossed, with welded bars, so as to give it not only the buoyancy of a life preserver, but almost incalculable strength. The facing of this floor is pine. Two men are usually placed at each of the wheels, so that eight are enabled to steer her; and four auxiliary wheels can be added, by which a force of thirty-two men can be brought to bear. Only four, however, are now guiding her through the calm, mild weather of the morning. The course is given by the first officer, the man next the compass guides the motions of the rest; and if the direction of the ship requires a sudden change, an auxiliary compass, or indicator, which receives its impulse from the central bridge, directs them immediately what to do. But for this device it would be difficult to guide the ship without great loss of time; but now orders are communicated from end to end with the speed of light, and the leviathan answers to her rudder and points its nose as readily as if drawn with a hook, 'or led' by its tongue with a cord.

At noon, as the bugle summoned us to lunch, I timed the paddle-piston at ten revolutions and the propeller at thirty and a half, and the log at the same time reported twelve and a half knots. The run of the ship for the last twenty six hours was reported as three hundred miles. Latitude 49°27', longitude 8°45'. When we came up from lunch we found that a light breeze had set in upon our larboard quarter, and our jib and forward trysails were spread to take advantage of it. The wind freshened as the afternoon grew on, and at three o'clock the billows began to crispen at their tops and indicate a rising sea. At four o'clock a drizzling rain set in, and the still strengthening wind gave promise of a stormy night. Some of us had been apprehensive, from the mild manner in which we had set out, that the voyage might run through the entire length of its term in the same dull way, and thus, while it deprived us of the least possibility of becoming heroes, land us at New York without any further knowledge of the ship and her sea-going qualities than we could have learned by studying her while anchored in the Thames. The fear of such disappointment, however, was dispelled by the time we had wiped our beards from dinner, for on ascending to the deck at six o'clock and taking our position on the elevated grating in her bow, we saw the leviathan, before so dead, so apparently inert, and which had been passing through the waters like some spectral island, quicken with life and bend with a slow grandeur to the motion of the sea. 'Thank God, she rolls!' exclaimed an experienced officer on her first trial trip, when she was caught in a series of heavy billows off Portland Race, and it was with something like the same ebullition of delight that we saw the mighty ship cast her silent disposition off and make her obeisance to the still mightier deep. Her motion was a gentle and majestic swing from side to side, the extent of three or four degrees, and now and then when a billow fell away from her bow and a swell at the same time would roll underneath her stern she would mildly yield her head,—not short and sudden, with a plebeian start, but with a monarch's measured grace, as if she felt herself to be the master, and only yielding to the courteous laws of life. It was a great treat to see her thus leaning her way from side to side through the parting waters, while good-sized ships, which were then in sight, were rolling uneasily or pitching from stem to stern. It was like some accomplished swimmer, who sweeps forward gracefully hand over hand, compared to a clumsy novice who barely manages to keep himself afloat through the rapidity of a short digging motion. The 'Great Eastern' was alive; but mighty as she was, still she was amenable to that vast throb and pulsation of the sea which is mightier than the mightiest. Nevertheless she proved, by the comparison before us, her superiority to all ordinary ships, as well as to any disturbing motion. In fact, her soft undulations gave actual relief and pleasure to every one who stood upon her deck. And all the while this motion was upon her the skittles were played at one of the after-holds. Nevertheless, let it be noted here that the theory that ships above a certain size will march through the wave superior to the perturbation of the sea is ended by our experiment forever. No ship can be made large enough to entirely ignore the gigantic pulsation of the ocean. The foresail and fore-topsail were drawing well at dark, and the wind, which now struck us almost astern, was whistling through our cordage with great noise.

A GALE. Tuesday, January 19, I was awakened a little after midnight by the howling of the wind, the shouts of the men taking in sail, and a great tramping overhead. The vessel was rolling more than she had at any time before,—say about eight or nine degrees,—and I could now feel a little vibration of her bow, imparted by the screw as it smote and scudded into the water whenever the motion of the vessel lifted its blades above the surface. I went to my window, but the night was too thick for anything but darkness to be seen, and all I could distinctly hear was the measured wail of one hundred and twenty men (for both watches had been called up) in chorus, to 'haul the bowline, haul,' while engaged in trying to take in the mainsail and main-topsail. The wind seemed to soften a little at two o'clock, but perhaps that was the notion of my drowsiness, for I fell asleep at that hour, while the men were still as busily engaged at the mainsail as ever. I afterwards learned that it had employed them five hours to furl it in the furious tempest that prevailed. The cause of this difficulty was partly owing to the violence of the gale acting upon the immense area of the sail, and partly to the unhandy size of the tackle by which it must necessarily be worked. Everything is exaggerated in the way of size on board the 'Great Eastern,' and to be handled aloft as other ships she requires an extra breed of men. The gale subsided a little in its fury at four o'clock, but when I arose, at seven, I still found it blowing very hard, and the sea covered with a thread-like foam, which filled the hollows as well as whitened on the billow tops. Still the ship rolled only eight degrees, and her stately nod did not disturb a plate upon the table. The storm-rack was laid at breakfast to protect the dishes, but it was not needed, for my full tea-cup sat outside of it without being in the slightest peril of a slip. Nevertheless, a three-thousand-ton vessel would have been pitching sadly. The motion did not succeed in making a single person sea-sick, though there were among her passengers several who had never been to sea before.

The wind moderated still more during the afternoon, and we set all our topsails, but the ship kept up her motion, and went frolicking along her path as full of life as a clipper-brig or a pilot-boat. Nothing could be more beautiful than to stand upon an elevated grating in her bow and see her stern lift itself majestically against the sky as we dropped into some yielding wave before us, or to behold her rising sideways to her equilibrium, like some frolicking beauty lifting her shoulder in her downy bed.... The most striking idea of her size, however, and the greatest demand upon your wonder that she swims so lightly, is obtained by going down by her sponsons, outside and aft the paddle-boxes, which enables you to see her entire towering section abaft the wheel. From that point you face up and down her massive sides and see the black warehouse, for it looks not like a ship, grandly rise and fall in the hissing and downy foam which the wheels send flying by her run. This flying foam unites beneath her stern, and is there strewn into lacework by the propeller, and goes seething on its broad path for miles. I think the scene from this lower platform of the gangway gives the finest idea, while in motion, of the vast power and grandeur of the ship. The deck and rigging, on the other hand, being seen altogether, lose in a little while their command upon the wonder, for their great symmetry so wins upon the eye that they mingle together in apparently usual degrees. It is only when in comparison with some other object that the 'Great Eastern' sensibly exhibits her huge proportions to an accustomed eye, and then everything else is dwarfed by her neighbourhood.

Wednesday, June 27. Fine weather, with a breeze which kept four of our trysails set, continued during the afternoon, but at six o'clock a very heavy fog set in, which condensed itself upon the rigging in huge drops that fell upon the deck like rain. So dense did this all-pervading mist become that the lookouts could scarcely see ten feet from the ship, and our lights could not have been distinguished at the distance of a hundred yards ahead; so out of mercy to the unwary who might possibly be in our path, at near reach to shore, we slackened our speed down from fifteen to seven and a half knots, and ran at this rate, with frequent warnings from our whistle, all night. Under this state of affairs it was thought prudent, moreover, that we should make soundings to ascertain with certainty exactly where we were, but the effort failed at every attempt, in consequence of the great height we were above the water, requiring more line than we could pay out while the vessel was in motion. We slowed her down to six knots, then to four and then to two, but still it would not answer, and the order went from the captain that the ship must be absolutely stopped.

It had been the particular pride of Mr McLennan, the chief engineer, who is a perfect enthusiast in his duty, that the ship's engines, which had been so much abused and misrepresented for the last year, should perform what scarcely, if ever, had been done before: and that was to make a first Atlantic voyage without a single moment's pause from port to port. When, therefore, he heard the order to stop the ship he received it like a man who was smitten with a sentence, and asked with the greatest earnestness if we could not get along without. The answer was against him, and the lungs of the monster were folded from their respirations, and after ten minutes' run with silent wheels and blades, and final reversal of her wheels, she sat still upon the waters. This event took place at 11.40, but a cast of one hundred and fifteen fathoms of line gave us no bottom, and we went on again, at twelve o'clock, still, however, continuing only at half speed. At ten minutes to five this morning we made another pause to heave the lead again, and this time with a cast of sixty-five fathoms we found bottom on George's Bank, and at ten minutes past five went on again. The fog having lifted, we now resumed our speed and proceeded at our usual rate of thirteen and fourteen knots. During these two pauses the engineer rapidly examined such of the screws and nuts as were not accessible during the action of the engines, but did not discover one that was out of place or that required tightening,—a great proof of the excellence and condition of her machinery.

Thus ended the first transatlantic voyage of the 'Great Eastern', and though it may be regarded as a failure in the way of speed, it will be perceived there were interests at stake which transcended that consideration, and which doubtless justified the commander in the unusual care he took to keep the great ship safe.

Captain Vine Hall is one of the most experienced navigators of the English East India trade, but in addition to the caution which he naturally felt incumbent on him from the fact that he had never crossed the Atlantic before, he was doubtless deeply impressed with the paramount importance, not only to his employers and the cause of science, but to England and the whole world, of giving a substantial proof that ships of the size of the 'Great Eastern' could safely cross the deep. It was therefore properly a matter of secondary consequence to him whether the enthusiasm of his passengers or the ardor of his engineers or officers should chafe at his divergences or extra care; he accomplished the great point that was required, and we who left England with him but ten days before are here to approve his action. When he returns to England in September he will give the leviathan its head, and she will then prove for herself that speed is one of her attributes as well as safety. In fact, she has proven it already by the manner in which she has accomplished this voyage, and there is not a passenger who crossed in her but views her as beyond all comparison the most superior passenger-ship that ever floated. The extra distance which she ran on this trip is certainly equal to more than a day's travel, and when we add to this that twenty-four hours' margin is always allowed to a new ship's first voyage, and take into consideration also that not an officer on board ever made a voyage in her, that the men were all raw recruits, fresh levied within three days of starting, and that even the stokers did not know how to spread coal to advantage on the fires, we cannot help regarding even the *time* she made as a great triumph. As to her comfort and convenience as a passenger-ship, it is hardly possible to say too much in praise of her. She meets all the requirements of the most luxurious hotel, and when the weather drives her inhabitants below they can promenade through her cabins upon long walks, or lounge about superb divans, listening to music that would not discredit the most pretentious concert. By her continued steadiness sea-sickness is entirely ignored, and in the way of strength no iron structure that ever has been made can at all compare with her.

This was impressed upon us by every sway of the sea, and the idea which she continually enforces on the mind, above all others, is her absolute safety from all ordinary dangers of the ocean. Against the risks resulting from contact with a solid body she is beyond all calculation stronger than anything which has been seen afloat. The manner in which her vast weight stood poised upon two single rests in the builder's yard for weeks before her launch, and the thundering against her sides of the huge battering-rams that smote her inch by inch towards the water, give evidence of what she can endure. No shoal or beach could break her before all her passengers could escape, for 'her scales are her pride, shut up together as with a close seal. They are joined one to another, they stick together that they cannot be sundered.'

Above all other ships she should be chosen by the timid, and it really is a puzzle to me how so many intelligent men who had read the history of her construction, and who were about crossing to New York at the date of her departure, could be induced to choose any other vessel. She is certainly exempt from all the ordinary dangers of the sea, and any one will go into her bow and look at the fourteen feet of matted iron in that welded beak, will credit her with sufficient power and impulse to split and push aside any ordinary iceberg.

As the sun rose in the sky on the morning of her arrival at Sandy Hook, the great ship was found anchored to await the tide which, between three and four in the afternoon, would give her enough depth to navigate the bar. Every passing ship circled round her and, as word passed from lip to lip along the shores of the bay, vantage points were crowded with an expectant throng. John Yates, who had proceeded ahead of the ship to arrange for her stay in New York, was early on the scene with the agents and their friends, in a chartered tug. Scores of small boats set sail to seek her out and some of the passenger steamers with their tall superstructure and beam engines prepared to make excursions at one dollar a time. There was nothing half-hearted about New York's welcome, nor the weather, warm, sunny and joyful. The ship's band, mounted uncomfortably on the hot paddle box, played innumerable renderings of 'Hail Columbia' in return for the strains of 'God Save the Queen', 'Rule Britannia', etc, which wafted over the water from all sides. To the handful of passengers high on the deck of the proud ship, the clear view of the long harbour, set off by myriad gaily coloured craft vainly seeking a breath of wind, their bunting reflecting tortuously from the ripples, was entrancing and, for some at least, unforgettable. To the sailors, and to those familiar with ships, the long black hull of the *Great Eastern* had lines of exquisite grace. As she moved slowly and easily towards the beckoning city, capricious rainbows radiating from the giant paddle boxes and lacing through the broad, soapy wake, a tumult of cheers, horns and bells, punctuated by cannon, followed her. Nothing revealed her size so much as when she passed the US frigate *Niagara*, hitherto the largest vessel in the world, courteously dressed in flags and streamers, as also was the Cunarder *Asia*, which fired salutes from her dock at Jersey City. As the giant visitor approached her mooring place under the control of Mr Murphy, the senior pilot of the port who had joined the ship in England, she turned to steam up river, proudly displaying her gargantuan glories to the expectant populace lining the surrounding vessels and shores, then imperiously returned to her destination, the quay at Hammond Street, where 'she was moored with hawsers as easily as one of the Cunard packets' and where she continued to be the cynosure of all eyes until darkness fell. This was her finest hour, all the struggles and tears forgotten and many of the expectations practically fulfilled.[3]

The New York vendors and showmen lost no time in following the crowds, nor were the property owners in the vicinity slow to let their spare ground at fabulous prices to the erectors of refreshment booths, and of tents for shooting galleries, 'Menagerie of Bears', the 'Great French Giant', and the like. Iced lemonade was sold, 'made from lemons grown on board the big ship', at one cent per glass, 'Great Eastern' cakes, candies and so on. No county fair was ever better purveyed or decorated. Turnstiles were installed at the head of two large gangways to regulate the entrance and exit of the throngs expected to make a tour of the ship at one dollar per head beginning at the advertised hour of 9.00am on Tuesday 3 July, just in time for the

fourth of July holiday. The intervening Sunday was particularly sol-
emnized on board by the funeral service for one of two stokers who,
in their separate ways, had fallen from the ship. It was an appropriate
occasion for a sermon on the evils of drunkenness. One old Englishman invited by an officer to have a preview of the ship by moonlight
was so moved by the experience that, on ascending to the top of the
great paddle box, he asked his friend to hold his stick, then plumped
down on his knees, his white hair glistening, and his hands clasped,
exclaiming "This is the proudest moment of my long life! God I
thank Thee I'm an Englishman!" This epitomized the sentiment of
the English community of the world, let alone of New York, and it
was often the target of much of the American press, and certainly of
the *New York Times*, which, in common with its rivals, made the
most of every opportunity to twist the lion's tail and exploit with
ridicule every embarrassment of British aspirations, whether in prize
fighting or maritime adventure. Nevertheless, they were ready to acknowledge sterling worth wherever it could be recognized, and there
were aspects of the great ship which easily warranted this. Unfortunately its management and fate were not among them. The interest in
the monster, however, was intense and widespread; great size was
something that even the meanest mortal could appreciate and thousands travelled from far and near to see this prodigious manifestation. 'Well,' said one stout woman from up country, 'of all the big
things I ever saw that's the biggest.' And in this she spoke for
hundreds of her compatriots.

5
THE EMBARRASSED DEBUTANTE

The great ship was spruced up, painted and polished, in preparation for her visitors. But while several thousands came to gaze, by boat and streetcar, and carriage after carriage arrived from the large hotels, only 1,700 actually paid their dollar to go aboard. The press thought the charge excessive, and *Scientific American* expressed the conviction that the cause of science would be better served by a lower charge to enable many more people actually to see the great engines and fine engineering appointments of the ship. The holiday spirit of the glorious fourth of July was appropriate to the occasion, and the crew of the great ship were treated to an exhibition of inimitable Yankee horseplay and holiday frolic. This, to English observers particularly, seemed the natural expression of American character, just as did the feud between New York fire-engine companies 21 and 13 which climaxed in a fight on the evening of the holiday. The vehicles of the rival companies collided with, or rammed, each other on their way to the same fire. Everything that lay to hand was used as a weapon—wrenches, crowbars, trumpets, stones and pistols—as they attacked each other with incredible ferocity. As many as a dozen shots were heard in the course of the *mêlée* which lasted until exhaustion intervened, a mere ten minutes, by which time a policeman had arrived on the scene. The names of the more seriously injured suggests that Irish blood, no less than Yankee, was involved. Some of the same spirit was revealed by a visitor to the ship who was ordered out of the purser's office where he was found leafing through an account book on a desk. With the remark that he had paid his dollar to see everything aboard the ship, and that he intended to do so, he moved to leave, then seized from the wall a large glazed frame containing the printed ship's regulations and threw it with all his force in the direction of his ejector. As the *Herald* reporter remarked, the officer, a gentleman, had the forbearance not to shoot the ruffian on the spot.

When the admission charge was halved, the numbers of visitors to the ship progressively increased to a maximum of about 18,000 on one day. This inspired the *Herald* to comment:

Reader, do you want to see a crowd? To be squeezed, reduced, contracted and epitomized, dovetailed and wedged in; to be scowled at by women and anathematized by men; to have your uninsured corn plantations remorselessly trod upon, and to groan in the very vexation of spirit thereat, to have parasols stuck in your eyes, and elbows in your ribs; your hat smashed, your bosom mussed ... to take your wife and daughter to see the show and be treated to intermittent glimpses of it between your neighbours' legs or over the summits of their heads? ... If so, go on board the Great Eastern.

The directors, through an agent, arranged several railway excursions from far and near and a blind man came all the way from Wisconsin to 'feel' the monster. Deputations from the towns of Philadelphia and Norfolk, Virginia, called on the captain to present the claims of their respective towns for a packet service with Liverpool, and at least to encourage a visit from the largest ship in the world. This interest was not new. In 1857, while the great ship was still on the stocks, railway entrepreneurs in the south had pressed the Great Ship Company to run their ship to Chesapeake Bay and assured it of a return cargo.[1] In the following year, A.D. Mann, a prime mover in the proposal, managed to establish a company in Virginia to build a fleet of large ships for the trade; but not much progress had been made by the time the *Great Eastern* sailed to America. Shortly after she arrived, the Baltimore and Ohio Railroad Co offered 2,500 tons of coal in return for a visit to Chesapeake Bay. First, however, it was planned to send her on a two-day excursion to Cape May, where Chesapeake Bay meets the sea. At the same time, the return voyage to England was advertised for 16 August, first-class passengers only at a fare of $120.

The excursion was arranged for 31 July, leaving at 3.00pm and arriving at Cape May, 'one of the most fashionable watering places in America', sufficiently early next day to allow time ashore before returning that evening to arrive in New York on 2 August. Food and refreshments would be available on board at moderate prices. Mattresses only, it was stated, would be provided for men 'in the various compartments and decks of the ship'. The state rooms, apparently, were being reserved for the ladies. Music would be provided by Dodsworth's celebrated band, both 'military and cotillon'.

A few days before the excursion, the *Great Eastern* was removed from the wharf and anchored nearby, no doubt to curtail expenses as she was prepared for her novel task and to facilitate her departure. The mayor of New York led a judicial party and a group of guests aboard a harbour steamer to conduct the hanging of a convicted criminal on Bedloe's Island. He instructed the captain to take a detour so that the hanging party and the condemned man, who sailed with them, could view the phenomenal ship, a procedure in which the criminal was reported to have taken no less interest than his escorts; his 'callousness ... was remarkable', wrote the reporter for *Frank Leslie's Illustrated Newspaper*.[2]

About 1,500 adventurous people bought tickets for the cruise to Cape May and boarded the great ship in festive mood on the day. Among the jornalists assigned to the trip was A.L. Holley, persuaded somewhat against his will, for he deplored the prostitution of the ship and the hopelessness of the directors who saw this as its only utility. But on account of the great ship's proneness to accident, the *New York Times* wanted an expert on the spot should the boilers burst or the paddles fall off. It was the usual warm, humid weather for the height of summer, and, if anything, there were even more people assembled all along the shores and on every vantage point, back into the countryside as far as eye could see, and more pleasure craft circling round in the blue waters, and more noisy, heavily laden passenger steamers in the wake, than on the memorable day of her arrival. It was one thing to see a mammoth standing still and quite another to see it actually moving of its own accord. Few expected it to move so sweetly and composedly and the appreciation resounded on every hand. One seasoned correspondent said that it would have taken the brush of Turner and the pen of a Byron to do justice to the glorious scene from the high, spacious steady deck of the monster ship. The excursionists aboard the ship commandeered every vantage point, some even in the tops and others scattered throughout the rigging, while the bulwarks were lined shoulder to shoulder.

Expectations and excitement ran high as the pilot was dropped at the bar off Sandy Hook and the ship churned onwards with her paddles drumming and her screw thrusting. The flotilla of escorts dropped behind one by one, sounding good-bye. Suddenly the throng realized that it was hungry and almost as one descended upon the dining facilities. This, however, proved altogether too much for the resources of management and supply, to say nothing of the goodwill or abilities of the waiters recruited for the excursion by the caterer. Many were rascals, others merely intoxicated, and the few who tried to do their duty found the going difficult. They could scarcely convey a trayful of viands without its being depleted by a cloud of grasping hands. Many had come on board fully expecting to be fed at no additional cost and were greatly discomfited to discover the true nature of things. For those who struggled for a place in the dining saloons, there was consequently very poor service. On top of this the coffee gave out and other scarcities multiplied along with a black market. 'It cost half a dollar merely to breathe the passing incense of a cup of coffee,' one reporter recorded. It did not help when irate diners addressed some of the waiters as 'niggers' and made boastful threats such as 'if I had you down South' and the like. One genteel fellow complained that when he asked one waiter for a cup of coffee for his lady, the waiter told him to go to Hell and sped off 'as if he were going to tear the kitchen down'. The carver in the second dining saloon became so overwhelmed that he laid down his knife and cleared out in disgust. The ice water became scarce and stores were damaged by a burst steam or water pipe. Some of the passengers were thankful for small mercies, however, and others had prudently carried aboard provisions of their own.

The search for state rooms had begun almost from the moment of departure and here again some thought that they would be able to procure cabin accommodation on board. Confusion also arose through the misappropriation of some rooms, and as the evening progressed there developed such a dire shortage of mattresses that no possessor of one could leave it unattended and expect to find it when he returned. Many gallant gentlemen in desperation to procure accommodation for their ladies searched for Mr Bold, the director in charge, or Mr Yates, to whom they were referred. But these gentlemen, and Mr Gooch, made themselves scarce in the face of mounting chaos. It did not help them that the newspapermen were not allotted berths.

Scores, however, had no thought of rest or retreat. The band, or parts of it, played for dancing. Revellers toured the ship until after midnight while more and more dropped out to find a mattress and a quiet corner. Mattresses, so recently unobtainable, now mysteriously became available at 50 cents and soon there was not a cabin top, nor a coil of rope nor an up-ended table, unoccupied by sleepers. The lone stewardess, a doughty Scotswoman, defended the Ladies'

Saloon, where shawl-covered figures could be seen sprawling under tables and on the floor, the children arranged in rows on the sofas.

Two men were unfortunate enough to select a sheep cage on deck as a retreat and to be locked in it by a party of promenaders who good-naturedly baited them in the juvenile humour of the time, and announced to the gathering crowd: 'Here, gentlemen, are some of the most extraordinary freaks of nature—animals that won't live upon the land and are bound to die in water. We have fed 'em on seventeenth proof whisky, which one man shoots into them with a double-barrelled squirt gun, while another holds their legs—a most interesting spec-ta-cle. Only five cents, and the refreshments thrown in. Feeding time in fifteen minutes,' and so on. Another group of revellers jumped on top of a mattress which two sleepers were using as a quilt and about fifty youths set out on a mattress race, the mattresses on their backs, while in a suitable space a score or so danced to music provided by some members of Dodsworth's strings and interspersed it with gymnastics. An hour or so of this moonlight revelling, of performing contests and horseplay, and there was peace at last, the participants bestrewn in all sorts of attitudes from bow to stern.

But it was not for long. By six o'clock the rising sun made sleep difficult on deck and aroused all and sundry. This time it was the ship's turn to be joker. She had deposited a layer of fine soot and ash over the deck which, mingling with the heavy dew—some say it rained— formed an oily scum upon the unsuspecting sleepers and their equipment. It was so many tired, begrimed, hungry, thirsty and fretful porcupines, as one observer put it, who arose from the mattresses. They cast about with grit-filled eyes for a place to wash and looked overboard, expecting to see the reassuring prospect of land. What was their dismay to find fresh water in short supply, whether for washing or drinking, and nothing in sight but the broad and blue uninterrupted ocean. Few knew it at the time, but an officer had mistakenly taken the ship fifty miles too far out to sea. It was not pleasant to feel so uncomfortable and tired in bright sunlight. A group of the more literate, mainly the newspapermen, held a meeting of indignation and drew up derogatory resolutions for publication in the New York papers.

By about seven o'clock the ship had moored at her destination; but because of the shallows this had to be at least six miles offshore. A further two hours expired before the expected tender arrived from Cape May to take off those who wished to spend the day there. Many trippers had gathered at the Cape in the expectation of seeing the great ship but only her indistinct outlines and masts, likened to a hedge on the horizon, could be seen. Several pleasure steamers brought sightseers from Philadelphia and other points on the Delaware Bay to the number of about four or five thousand, one hundred of whom decided to return to New York with the ship, officially and some unofficially. These took the place of the disgruntled excursionists and newspapermen who preferred to return to New York by train. It was a normal hot day, and ice water—a standard commodity aboard all excursion steamers on that coast—soon ran out again, although a further supply of ice had been shipped from one of the tenders. The steamers transferred their passengers to the *Great Eastern* with difficulty in the heavy swell and the bottom end of the companion way was soon crushed and splintered.

Meantime, as the day drew on and the tender did not arrive at the scheduled time to return them, the excursionists who had spent the day at the Cape grew anxious. When an hour had passed and there was still no sign of the tender, Cyrus W. Field, who was one of this number and who was destined to play an important part in the future of the *Great Eastern,* chartered a small steamboat to return himself and family and the forgotten excursionists to the distant ship.

By about six o'clock, the last visitors, with no little trouble and commotion, had left and the excursionists were happy to be rid of the hubbub and crush and have the ship to themselves again. The anchor was raised and the great ship got under way with much satisfaction all round. The catering was but little improved and even the directors and their friends had largely to help themselves. It was a balmy night and there was dancing and singing but most of the jokers were tired out, although there were still a few rowdies, and one objectionable pack of roisterers in particular ran along the deck with mattresses on their backs awakening sleepers to ask them if they had had their $10 worth. If the answer was 'yes'—all right—if 'no', they were urged to rouse themselves and make up for it. But even this indefatigable pursuit of enjoyment had to end, and when dawn revealed the familiar skyline of New York there were many rejoicing hearts, many disgruntled and indignant with their experience, and many conscious of its historic character and ready to make allowances which were scarcely deserved.

The journalists obtained their revenge, and Bennett's *Herald,* which was the mildest of the critics, declared that 'a general famine would have overwhelmed all hands if the ship had been a meal and a half away from land'. The numerous minor publications of New York were the most scurrilous and officers of the ship were requested to reply to some of these attacks, and particularly, in the words of one officer, to 'such malicious abuse as fills the dirty columns of such trash as *Harper's Weekly*... Weeds such as these should have no place among the blooming flowers of the New York press: they should be plucked up and cast into the fire.'

The eminent engineer, A.L. Holley, was chagrined at the abuse of a great engineering achievement and wrote what we may regard as the last word on the subject:

... the valuable Directors of the Great Ship Co have at last succeeded in damming up the flood tide of popular favor which greeted the noble work of Russell and Brunel and of involving this whole scheme of improved navigation, with its intrinsic excellencies and its unworthy excrescences in promiscuous disgrace. No sooner had the *Great Eastern* developed the mechanical practicability of large ships ... no sooner had the idea of her remarkable comfort and safety, and her probable success become popularized, than these adventurers must needs turn the noble vessel into a sewer before two thousand citizens at a time, belying the hopes and promises of her real friends ... who draw a distinct and indelible line between the *Great Eastern* as an engineering construction, and the *Great Eastern* as the 'attraction' of these itinerant showmen.[3]

No time was wasted in cleaning up the mess aboard the *Great Eastern* and preparing for the trip to Hampton Roads and Annapolis next day. A mere 105 passengers boarded for this jaunt. The drop in interest of the public was attributed to the bad press given the excursion to Cape May. But a lesson had been learned and, of course, it was easier to cater for 105, especially when more were expected. The fare was $8 to Annapolis and $6 to Hampton Roads. 'Good-bye sweet city of fires and pistol practice', sardonically whispered one officer to himself as the great ship sailed off with hardly a glance from the erstwhile enthusiasts of the harbour. Exactly twenty-four hours later the ship stood off Hampton Roads and fired 'four guns'—four shots from the signal cannon which all large ships then carried, then a further thirteen in response to eleven from the fort. The captain and officers graciously declined an invitation to sample Virginian hospitality tendered by a deputation of gentlemen from Norfolk. There was a strong desire in these southern ports to establish a regular steamer link with England.

Next day, Saturday 4 August, about 4,000 people paid 50 cents to visit the ship, including some slaves—'appearing well clad, well fed, and clean'. Early on the Sunday morning, the patient monster headed into Chesapeake Bay to anchor around 5.00am, at a depth of about seven fathoms almost in the middle of the bay, six miles off Annapolis. The Bay Line of steamers which gifted the coal, naturally had the monopoly of transporting to the ship the visitors who now converged upon her from all the towns along the bay. The weather was oppressively warm and hardly comfortable for the loading of coal from the six colliers lying in attendance. Fortunately, the coal hatches were on the side of the ship and coaling could proceed without too much nuisance. Some of the rowdies coming aboard, however, made up for it. One particular group picked a quarrel in the bar, and the resulting *mêlée* involved the waiters and members of the crew. The boarders were repelled leaving one of the most ferocious of their number in irons. The ringleader insulted an American lady in the presence of her husband, who held his peace and awaited his return to shore before taking out a revolver and shooting the offender dead on the wharf, in full view of everyone. These summary acts of vengeance, noted one of the officers, were common in that country. The same officer, along with some of his fellows, took the opportunity to land at Annapolis and visit Baltimore. Aboard the train, he remarked on the casual manner in which many of the travellers perched themselves on the engine tender to which the conductor observed, 'I guess if they get chawed up 'taint no fault of ours.'

At Baltimore, they were taken to see Winant's novel cigar ship which had the form of a modern submarine, 235ft × 16ft, but was propelled by a paddle sandwiched amidships. One of these vessels was built by Scott Russell's foreman, Hepworth, in the David Napier yard which Russell abandoned in 1862, but they did not find favour. The officers also had an interesting visit to the largest tobacco factory in the States—Messrs Gail and Ax—where they saw all the men smoking at their work. Some, as a result, smoked without ceasing the whole day through. One of these men, smoking and exposed to tobacco dust day after day, it was noted with interest, lived to the age of eighty-six after being many years in the factory.

On his return to the ship, the officer found the excursionists squeezing and fighting, screeching and yelling to get aboard with such abandon that a few of the more timid preferred to remain all night and be taken off in the daylight. At 10.30am on the 9th, Presi-

Part of the dining saloon, photographed while anchored at Quebec in July 1861
(*Notman Archives, McCord Museum of McGill University*)

Captain William Harrison, the first captain of the *Great Eastern*, who drowned in Southampton Harbour in January 1860 (*Illustrated London News*)

Captain James Anderson, who was knighted for his captaincy of the *Great Eastern* when the first transatlantic cable was laid (*Illustrated London News*)

dent Buchanan and his party visited for two hours, arriving to the accompaniment of a twenty-one gun salute and the music of Yankee Doodle; the great ship was never short on ceremony. It was strange to British ears to hear the President accosted by some of the crowd with 'Well, Mr President, how d'ye do? Glad to see you; guess you're looking sprig', and so on. Another of this concourse addressed a ship's officer with 'Mr Officer, I guess this ship's a great humbug.' To which the officer quickly retorted, 'That's the opinion of every fool that's seen her.'

The *Great Eastern* returned to New York with thirty-four passengers paying $20, including provisions this time, arriving on Sunday 12 August with little ceremony. The interest in the ship had markedly declined and the *Herald* remarked that no one expected to see her in New York again. 'We all know', the editor continued, 'that there is not sufficient trade between New York and any European port' to justify it. A writ was served against the ship for infringement, of an American patent taken out on the propelling of a ship by a combination of screw and paddles. Her trafficking in domestic waters had made her liable; but after some anxiety, the writ was deemed invalid. Hence, on Thursday 16 August, the maritime wonder of the day was able to turn her bow to sea again and leave the scene of her triumph and embarrassment with 102 passengers (46 for Halifax) to the accompaniment of but a few guns and cheers. She had overstayed her welcome. *Harper's Weekly* expressed it thus:

'It is time, we think, that the *Great Eastern*—or, at all events, her directors, officers, and crew—went back to their own country. They are charming people; but we have seen them, and paid our money, and we need say no more about it. In England, perhaps, they are the right men in the right place; if *we* had a ship like the *Great Eastern,* we should try to put at least one or two people on board who had the manners of gentlemen and the civility of Christians. But let them pass. When Frenchmen, Germans . . . say—as they all do—that they hate Englishmen because Englishmen are rude, coarse, boorish, mean, and pig-headed, we Americans are apt, for cousinship's sake, to stand up for poor old John, and put in a word for him. But we don't think it likely that any of the Americans who have experienced the tender mercies of the *Great Eastern* will have much to say in John's behalf hereafter.[4]

But one director, Daniel Gooch, tells us that he was never so glad to leave any place. He deplored the general dishonesty prevailing in business and the sharp practices even by the agents of the ship and, not least, the want of ability in Captain Hall and his officers to manage the internal matters of the ship. The captain was certainly 'mighty vain' and the officers cared more about showing themselves off about town. The expenses swallowed up a large part of the £20,000 accrued from about 165,000 visitors and the directors had not emerged unscathed.

The *Great Eastern* anchored in Halifax harbour forty-six hours after leaving New York, five-and-a-half hours within the shortest time on record. The expected crowds gathered to see her; but the port charged £350 for light dues despite protests and the ostensible wish to encourage the visit. The directors indignantly decided not to tarry and precipitately left at 8.00am next morning, Sunday 19 August, with seventy-two passengers and a desire to arrive home as soon as possible. The journey was uneventful and the ship revealed that she could roll in a heavy cross sea. On the seventh day, the coast of England hove into view and the happy vessel steamed imperiously through the wooden walls of the Channel Fleet to her anchorage off Pembroke where many of the passengers remained another night on board, so reluctant were they, it was said, to leave their comfortable quarters.

The average speed for the voyage was from 13 to 14 knots or 16 miles per hour. More was expected of her or perhaps, more accurately, hoped for her, and it was suspected that her hull was dirty, but when she was laid up for the winter on a gridiron on the beach at Milford Haven, this was not found to be so and many felt disappointed.

6

THE STRUGGLE FOR EXISTENCE

Proper allowance was not made by the *Great Eastern*'s critics for the disadvantages under which she laboured on her maiden voyage. There was understandable aversion to forcing the new engines and boilers, and in any case the stokers employed for the voyage, from all accounts, were an inexperienced and unskilled group of labourers. There is more to stoking a furnace than throwing on coal if minimum fuel consumption for maximum steam production is of concern. But the extravagant expectations of her speed reacted adversely upon the ship and, on the Atlantic run, she had to do better than 14 knots to shine.

The opportunity was now taken to attend to some deficiencies. Comments were made in the press about the porous nature of the deck planking. But the planking simply covered a completely iron deck. The wood had a bad appearance, however, and it was considered necessary to cover it with pitch and superimpose upon this a new surface of 2in pine planks. Of greater concern, however, was the stern bearing supporting the propellor shaft. The Babbitt-metal lining of this had been squeezed out at the bottom of the bearing. Joshua Field and John Penn were consulted and recommended that a liner of brass be shrunk on the shaft and an approximation of Penn's patent stern-tube bearing be contrived by forming the bearing surface of strips of lignum vitae, a very hard tropical wood which lubricated well with water, dovetailed into a brass tube. This was done under awkward circumstances and proved to be efficacious. New feed pumps were fitted and the funnels were painted bright red. The white line which was added to the decor of the ship prior to its maiden voyage was repainted, much to the annoyance of those who found the optical illusion it produced, of a hogged deck, intolerable. Everything was rectified which needed rectifying and even a little

extra damage was introduced on the recession of the tide, by allowing the bow to remain unsupported while overhanging the gridiron
with a heavy load of ballast water still in her. Brunel's former assistant, Brereton, was still the Company engineer.

Much was made by the Company of some of the deficiencies now
being made good. This, with the inadequate compensations of the
maiden voyage, said to have cleared about £14,000, left the finances
of the Company in their familiar state—'not very satisfactory'. In addition, the shares had continued to decline on the report that the
Grand Trunk Railway Co of Canada was about to claim £60,000
damages for breach of contract in having the ship sent to New York
instead of Portland as so long planned. Indeed, in March 1861, it was
announced that the next trip would be to the Southern States which
had but newly seceded from the Union. Captain Hall, manager Bold
and chief engineer McLennan and all but twelve of the crew had been
dismissed.[1] It was deemed necessary to raise £35,000 on debentures
at twelve months and 10 per cent. The Company was also refusing to
comply with the arbitrators' award of £18,000 to John Scott Russell,
announced in the previous August. They claimed that the arbitrators
had exceeded their jurisdiction, particularly in considering Russell's
claim in respect of extras ordered during the progress of the work.[2]
The appeal court ruled in favour of the Company, but, commenting
that it was a case of great difficulty, decided neither to enforce the
award nor to set it aside. Russell, thus left to his legal remedies,
brought a further action, as a result of which the Chief Justice found a
verdict in his favour, confirming the award of £18,000. The
Company appealed against this also, but there were rumours that the
ship was to be sold in America or to Napoleon III, and since she was
due to sail in three or four days time, Russell's solicitors did not tarry
but promptly took possession of the ship by Sherriff's warrant, as the
only security for the award. As *The Times* observed, Russell could
now have knocked down the ship to himself. When the Company
lost its appeal, they reluctantly paid up and retrieved the ship practically on the eve of its intended departure, 1 May.

The uncertainty played havoc with the bookings, and the wonder
was that there were as many as one hundred passengers assembled at
Milford Haven ready to embark on the appointed day. To further
test their optimism, the tender which carried them out to the ship ran
aground on approaching its goal and no amount of rocking—by the
passengers running from side to side—could free her. Small boats

were recruited to take off the marooned passengers and their baggage and the operation had barely begun when the rising tide and a pull on a hawser from the great ship freed the tender and brought her alongside. At last, with all aboard, including 7,000 tons of coal, the *Great Eastern* cast off her moorings and set out into the dusk with a new captain, W.B. Thompson, and a new Chief Engineer, Robertson. They were soon put to the test, when, about four days out, the ship ran into the worst storm she had yet encountered. It came as a genuine surprise to everyone that the monster ship, so contemptuous of seas which made lesser craft roll and pitch, could in fact meet a sea which would make her behave likewise. There had been hints of this, but not enough to provoke the usual seagoing precautions with furnishings and movables. For a time, tables were overturned and chairs scattered in a heap below decks. The rigging gave trouble, and there were some particularly anxious moments with a gaff which broke loose. This swung at the end of its chain, and viciously whipped the rigging and a funnel, and broke several skylights before being secured. It was a foretaste of what could be expected if the great mass were set rolling in synchrony with long waves in a really severe North Atlantic storm; but the warning was not taken too seriously, and there were many other things to think about.

There was continued talk of the ship's being procured by some government or other, that of the USA being the most likely, now that the Civil War had broken out. At the same time a rumour, essentially correct, reached the British Government that Seward the US Secretary of State, had proposed to Lincoln that the United States declare war on Great Britain and France as a means of bringing the southern states back into the Union. In reinforcement of this, the US Government, in several ways, seemed to be taking a very bellicose line with the British. This alerted the latter to the vulnerability of upper Canada. With commendable intelligence, the Admiralty quickly surveyed the *Great Eastern* on her return from New York, and chartered her to transport 2,500 troops and 200 artillery horses to Quebec. Her cargo spaces were quickly modified for the purpose and with wives and families and forty independent passengers, including William Froude, the aspiring naval hydrodynamist, and Henry Brunel, the younger son of the great engineer, there was a total of 3,400 people aboard. Yet another captain, James Kennedy of the Inman Line, was engaged to take command, and he conducted this unprecedented cargo out of Liverpool to the Atlantic where he virtually pointed the ship towards the St Lawrence and signalled full ahead through fog and ice fields indifferently.

With the *Great Eastern*'s usual luck, Kennedy could have anticipated the *Titanic* disaster; it was said that he missed the Cunard liner *Arabia* by little more than the length of a bowsprit in the fog off Cape Race. Nevertheless, ten days after leaving Liverpool the *Great Eastern* stood grandly and safely off Quebec and disembarked her precious freight. At least this was one voyage which paid handsomely. She remained off Quebec nearly a month entertaining sightseers and allowing time for bookings of 500 passengers for the return trip. Kennedy left for another appointment on the ship's return to Liverpool and was replaced by Captain James Walker for the last voyage of the year. Considering all the knowledge and qualities Brunel thought requisite in the commander of the novel machine called the *Great Eastern*, the turnover of captains is remarkable, as also was the apparent ease with which they seemingly handled the great vessel without even a practice run. To this, Captain Walker was no exception, indeed he had not even been aboard the ship until the day before sailing.[3] He was destined to remember his first and only voyage in the *Great Eastern* with special feeling.

Encouraged by the series of successful voyages and the fulsome recommendations of those who sailed in her, the *Great Eastern* at last seemed to have won her laurels and loaded up at Liverpool with a full complement of 400 passengers for the first time and more cargo than she had yet been assigned to carry. Little did anyone suspect the terrors which the great ship's jinx had in store for them as they watched her cast off her moorings on the afternoon of Tuesday 10 September, with all the usual interest of the populace. In the words of one passenger, W.H. Gibbs, a prominent Canadian businessman from Oshawa, who later became an MP:

We left Liverpool at 1.00pm ... with flying colours and tens of thousands of spectators. The sight was a grand and inspiring one to us and everyone on shore. The docks were covered with people for miles, forming by far the most imposing sight of the kind I ever witnessed. There could not have been less than 100,000 people assembled to see us off. In addition there were dozens of steamers full of sightseers and numerous displays of bunting, flags and gunpowder. It was exciting, a regular gala day, and we all felt big with our importance as passengers on the *Great Eastern*.[4]

The fare was £20 to £28 first class, and £7 to £10 steerage. Once clear of the Mersey, she turned south and at a steady 13 to 14 knots under full steam and sail, made good progress in the next two days, during which the breakfast tables were crowded to a degree which was thought novel by experienced voyagers. Children played hide and seek on the deck and ball in one of the holds, while the large New York packet *Underwriter* was speedily overtaken and left behind, pitching lamentably in the strong breeze, a breeze which ominously increased to gale force by about 4 o'clock of the afternoon of the second day out. The great ship now rolled to the punches of the heavy seas, and very soon one of the forward boats was torn loose such that it hung from one of its davits, flapping itself asunder against the ship. Things were becoming boisterous, but no one was alarmed. Captain Walker ordered the damaged lifeboat to be cut adrift. The helm was put down to bring the ship up into the wind and the paddle engines were stopped in order to avoid fouling the paddle with the abandoned boat, a fateful manoeuvre. Scott Russell wrote that the captain backed her with the rudder hard over and that this procedure would generally wring the rudder right out of a ship. Instead, in the case of the *Great Eastern,* the rudder head fractured. The rudder was considered too heavy to rest on its lower support pin alone and was therefore also supported by a collar keyed to the 14in rudder shaft, resting on large ball-bearings. The collar was held down on the balls by a huge nut screwed upon a thread cut in the shaft. The rudder head was of smaller diameter and, according to one account, was welded to the rudder shaft, a very uncertain method of joining two large masses of metal before the days of X-rays. The rudder head fractured at the neck of the junction of the two shafts, as one would expect, and no wonder the ship would not answer her helm when the captain ordered the paddle engines ahead again. The army of men at the helm would not feel the deficiency while they held it hard over, and hence it was not until the next morning that the failure was discovered. Meantime the ship rolled in the trough of the waves and several boats were carried off in rapid succession. A man and a boy crawled aboard the long boat to unravel its twisted tackle, an act of no little bravery or hardihood in the circumstances, for the boat was one moment almost in the waves then at another thrown high in the grip of the gale. During one of these oscillations, a violent gust ejected them on to the deck while the boat broke away and fell into the sea. In modern ships the boats are tucked in securely, but the *Great Eastern*'s boats protruded somewhat beyond the edge of the deck and were occasionally lapped by the waves at the end of a roll, especially in a beam sea, 'mountains' high.

After discovering on the previous voyage that the ocean was mightier than the *Great Eastern,* it is a wonder that her owners would not fasten down her furnishings; but she had again changed commanders and perhaps the new crew was incredulous that anything could rock a ship so immense. Certainly she had never been at the mercy of a heavy sea in a gale with her rudder disabled. Tables, couches and chairs tumbled and swung from one side of the grand saloon to the other, smashing and being smashed, sometimes pursuing and sometimes being pursued by passengers and stewards. Most devastating was the iron stove which broke adrift from the centre of the room and promptly 'starred' one of the large mirrors, followed by a pursuing passenger whose impact with the same mirror was accompanied by a shower of scintillating glass fragments which were gradually churned into atoms with indescribable noises of destruction. The hapless passenger had his head cut, a tooth knocked out and a finger dislocated. The grand piano also broke away and waltzed and twanged in an orgy of incredible abandon. Similar sights and sounds were encountered all over the ship, but, not surprisingly, the pantries and dining rooms offered a special spectacle with flying crockery, china, plate, cutlery and the like.

On deck, the struggle continued, eight boats in all were torn away or stoven in. Occasionally, the sea like a waterspout would surge up the side of the ship and collapse into a cataract which swilled all before it. The cow house was swept away and one of the two cows fell through the skylight of the ladies' saloon and had to be killed, the other died of its injuries.

For the most part, it seems, the rolling was slow and majestic, no creaking, shuddering or recoiling, some took courage from this and others thought it ominous, while the captain stood on the bridge struggling gallantly to keep an upright posture, and to appear calm and collected, holding the rails with all his strength. There was no panic and the initial terror gave way to more hopeful fear as the ship revealed no sign of weakness. A roll of sheet lead unfortunately tore itself free in the paddle engine room, and when it threatened to roll into the great oscillating cylinders Chief Engineer Roberston stopped the engine, while the crew attempted to capture and restrain the juggernaut. This took half an hour, after which the engine was started at half speed. It is a curious fact about paddles that they were rarely damaged by the sea while kept in motion but when they were held still they were too flimsy to take the unaccustomed stresses. So was it with the slender structure of the *Great Eastern*'s paddles and, when the engine started again, one of the paddles, apparently damaged, scraped against the side of the ship in a most threatening way. In consternation the engine was stopped again, whereupon the waves made short work of crossbars, floats and spokes. They were simply shorn off leaving but a stump, as with Tam o' Shanter's mare.

A jib sail was hoisted in an attempt to run the ship before the wind—no simple matter—but it was hardly up when it was ripped into ribbons with the sounds of artillery. Another attempt was made with a trisail and this lasted half an hour with no effect before ripping into shreds. Then thirty tons of chain broke loose and lashed horribly from side to side against the hull plates in the locker room in the bow sending terrifying crashing vibrations and thuds through the ship. At some point during this time it was found that the loose rudder was swinging against the propeller. The screw engine, therefore, also had to be stopped. Another effort was made to turn the ship's head with the remaining paddle but the floats of this had been too badly damaged and fell off. The greatest ship in the world was then literally powerless, adrift in the tempest without engines or sail, or rudder! Mr Gibbs wrote:

There seemed to be no hope for us, and night coming on added new terrors to our pitiable condition. I shall never to my last day forget the horrors of that night. Its horrors and terrors were much increased by the confusion in the cabins and saloons below. Everything in the interior of the ship seemed to have broken loose and gone to rack and ruin. The noise and commotion were terrific...

Friday dawned with somewhat moderated wind but with continued and frequently violent rolling of the ship making breakfast and dinner practically impossible, although many hardy souls attempted both, holding on to the tables and chasing cutlery and plates from time to time. The period of roll of the ship was coinciding with the period of the waves. According to Mr Gibbs, at worst the ship rolled up to seventeen times a minute. By this, he probably means it had eight or nine oscillations per minute, a period of 9.5 seconds. The effect of this on the main deck of such a large ship would certainly be dramatic. The whole face of the paddle boxes, he added, was submerged at the end of every swing. On one occasion, reported another observer, tables, chairs, crockery, passengers and stewards ended in an accumulation in the middle of the saloon, and since the baker was one of the increasing toll of casualties, there was no pastry or bread available. One must hand a bouquet to the galley crew for making such gallant efforts, and wonder at any passengers having an appetite at all. Open barrels of biscuits were lashed down at various places for the hungry.

Then it was discovered that a large proportion of the passengers' baggage which had been carelessly left unsecured in one of the cargo spaces was swimming in water. Trunks, portmanteaus and bags, thrown from side to side, hour after hour, gradually came apart and spilled out their contents to be quickly churned into a slurry of rags, shoes and sundries. Some men were later seen paddling in this with bare feet feeling for jewellery and money. Gibbs thought the destruction of the passengers' luggage 'was the most wanton since the most ordinary prudence would have saved it'. The whole ship's crew, he declared, 'seemed to be completely demoralized, without the least order or subordination. Nobody seemed to care about anything.' Two enormous iron tanks of oil, each weighing about two or three tons, rolled from side to side for a time in the crew's quarters smashing berths and the side of the ship. One report has it that they contained fish oil and that this was spilled all over the place. But whether true or not, there was enough trouble without it. The unrelenting rolling was becoming unendurable, so, with much relief, efforts were turned on deck to loading a large four-ton spar with iron and throwing it overboard attached to hawsers port and starboard. This was partially effectual in bringing the ship's head round and reducing the rolling.

A meeting of the passengers was held in the evening of this, the second day of their misfortunes. Resigned to the fact that the ship had drifted out of the track of vessels and that aid was probably days away, they formed a committee to liaise with the captain in the maintenance of discipline and the organizing of passenger co-operation. Gibbs tells us that there was danger of a mutiny in which officers and passengers would be pitted against the crew, the latter threatening to take possession of the stores and boats. The concerned passengers formed police squads to patrol the ship in threes night and day. Some stokers, it was said, in their idleness, had broken into the liquor stores and drowned their pummelled senses as only they knew how. It was the best way to go if go they must.

Chief Engineer Robertson had not been idle. He tried to loop a chain around the rudder stump, and by pulling the free ends by means of ropes and pulley blocks, to control the rudder shaft. But the chain slipped and made no impression on the rudder. An American engineer, Hamilton E. Towle, of Boston, who was returning from work in Europe, suggested that the chain be wrapped round the nut, or collar which supported the rudder on the ballbearings. This was 2ft 9in in diameter at the base and 15in at the top. The chief pooh-poohed the idea on the reasonable grounds that the chain would slip off the nut. Towle, however, countered this by proposing that successive coils of chain be wound round the collar and bound to it in such a way as to give a larger and more uniform diameter of drum on which the tiller chains could act. He showed a sketch of his proposal to the chief who curtly brushed it aside and proceeded upon his own plan.[5] This was to unscrew and remove the collar to obtain a greater length of shaft about which to wind the tiller chain. Fortunately, loosening the rudder nut was difficult, particularly when the rudder swung so erratically to the buffeting of the waves. When Towle learned of this, his alarm overcame his reticence and he went to the captain to warn him of the danger of losing the rudder altogether. The captain was too busy with his command of a ship without rudder or power in a heavy sea to give Towle an audience immediately; but after some hours he did so and was sufficiently impressed to make his way with Towle to the steering gear at the stern where he ordered or persuaded the chief to abandon his risky plan and allow Towle to effect his. First, however, Towle had to screw up the support nut in the same laborious way as that in which it had been loosened, that is, by holding it with a special key slung from an overhead timber and letting the force of the water on the rudder tighten it up in a series of bites, a process which took about three hours.

Meantime a heavy chain was procured and lowered through a hole specially cut in the main deck above, and the difficult task of winding it upon the collar began. Each coil of chain was lashed to the collar by a lighter chain laced through the holes in the bottom flange and built up until a chain drum, about 4ft in diameter, was constructed. The rolling of the ship made this task all the more difficult, throwing the loose chain about and requiring it to be restrained by an army of men. At eleven on the Saturday night, after about six hours of effort, Towle informed Robertson that his apparatus was ready. The latter asked that the chains be tightened to test their ability to hold the rudder against the impact of the sea and this was done. The chains creaked and trembled under the strain, but held. Robertson for some reason professed that he would have to see the apparatus endure these stresses for two or three hours before he would feel satisfied. Towle thought this ridiculous and went directly to the captain to tell him that he could now start the screw engine. Robertson advised the captain that Towle's apparatus could not be depended upon to hold but that with the help of another he was in process of

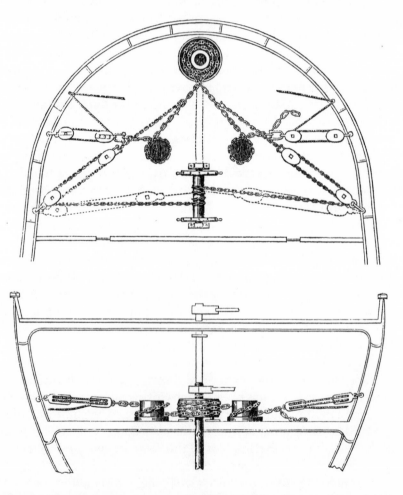

FIG 1 The temporary steering apparatus improvised by Hamilton Towle (*Scientific American*)

rigging up, it could perhaps be expected to succeed. His proposal was to pass a chain over the stern and round the rudder, catching it in a notch which impact with the propeller had gouged into the rudder's edge. The whole of Sunday was occupied in this labour and all to no avail, for the chain repeatedly slipped out of the notch. The brave seaman who volunteered to be lowered over the stern in a jury rig to help effect this operation was unceremoniously dunked in the chilly waves as they rose and fell; but was later recompensed by a grateful testimonial from the first-class passengers.

During this time, the uninvolved passengers were a prey to idleness, fear and rumour and, when, on the Saturday night the small brig *Magnet,* out of Halifax, appeared on the scene, attracted by the rockets and blue lights sent up by the stricken giant, she was regarded as an 'Angel of Mercy'. Although she could do no more than keep within sight, bobbing like a cork in the waves, this, strangely, had a reassuring effect on the weary and fearful passengers—the flea and the elephant indeed. 'We felt the *Magnet* might save a few souls if the ship went down', wrote Gibbs. That some of the more wealthy passengers offered immense sums of money to the crew of the *Magnet* to entice them to stand by all night, could be true; in which case the master of the gallant little craft may have recalled how Pate Birnie, an old Scottish fiddler, excused his ignoring of his promises to God made at the height of a recent illness—'Who pays attention to what a man says in a fever?' Perhaps, too, in the same way, God lent an indulgent ear to any like promises in the prayers of Mr Gibbs. But it is difficult to see how any messages could be transmitted from the one ship to the other in the circumstances. Nevertheless, the *Magnet* did not desert her station and did not part company with the great ship until in the astonishing calm of the Sunday, Captain Walker at last gave the order to proceed. Towle's rig held out well enough to turn the ship round and hold her on a course for Ireland about three hundred miles distant, at a steady 7 knots and to everyone's intense relief. It is gratifying to know that the passengers prepared a petition of thanks which they later forwarded to the owners and crew of the *Magnet,* the captain of which collected one day's demurrage.[6]

On the Monday, the crack Cunarder, the *Persia,* hove into sight and, obviously curious about the unexpected spectacle of the *Great Eastern* heading in the wrong direction, sailed right round her, no doubt observing the absence of the paddles and the signs of destruction on deck. A message written on a board was held up over the paddle box but the *Persia* could not edge near enough to read it nor to hear much of what was shouted at her. Since the *Great Eastern* did not slacken speed, the *Persia* then headed for New York scratching her head. Perhaps it was thought that the great and docile giant was too embarrassed to reveal her distress to a cock-a-hoop Cunarder.

Next morning she was off the Old Head of Kinsale making for Queenstown and a curt announcement in the London papers brought the news to the city. 'Great Eastern reported from Queenstown has lost her paddlewheels; rudder and steering gear damaged.' What a sensation. The long suffering John Yates and the new chairman of the Company, the Hon Captain Carnegie, instantly packed their bags and hastened to Cork. Further difficulties with the improvised steering made it necessary to head the ship out clear of the land. One can imagine the despair of the more emotionally exhausted passengers—and there must have been many, especially when a smart gale sprung up from the south-west and made it hazardous to attempt to bring the ship round at all under her crude steering rig. She was therefore propelled slowly back into the grey expanse for some hours until a change in wind made it safer to turn. But at least the ship was then again headed for the harbour. Darkness fell, and the more indestructible of the passengers amused themselves with surprising jollity. It was ironical that after such a week of danger and calamity it was only now, as the ship manoeuvred to enter the harbour in the morning, that a person was killed. A quartermaster was somehow struck in the head by a kick of the wheel and had his skull fractured.

By this time, Yates and Carnegie had arrived and were conducted out to the ship where they were briefed by the captain. They must have been relieved to find that only about thirty passengers had suffered significant injuries. They offered to refund the passage money or pay alternative passage in the steamer *Norwegian* from Liverpool. There was no talk of compensation for the baggage ultimately carried off the ship in pails. The *Great Eastern* was edged into the harbour threatening every nearby obstacle with her awkward movements. The passengers were landed at long last and the directors ordered that the ship be immediately prepared to become once more the object of a local excursion trade while repairs were set afoot. Mr Gibbs, much unnerved and suffering violent headaches, decided to spend a few days by the Lakes of Killarney to recover, before facing the continuation of his voyage aboard the Cunarder *Niagara*.

When Hamilton Towle reached New York, he claimed the salvage of the *Great Eastern*, and in November was decreed at law entitled to recover $15,000 from the Great Ship Company for his pains.[6] This must have made John Yates wince. It took about 24,000 visitors to the ship at half-a-crown a head to raise that sum.

After immediate repairs were effected at Queenstown, the *Great Eastern* was escorted by a tug to her anchorage at Milford Haven where the more substantial repairs were completed over the winter (1861–2), much to the detriment of the profits of the previous season. It could not have helped the directors' nerves when, in March, as the great ship was being swung with the tide at her anchorage, she collided with the frigate *Blenheim* and carried away the latter's bowsprit, jib boom, main yard and moorings. This had occurred in the confusion resulting from the fouling of the propeller by a crowded small boat, two of the occupants of which were drowned.[7] If the Company could have seen a way to release themselves profitably from their burden they would eagerly have done so. They had not given up hope, however, and three sailings were planned to New York for the season of 1862. A new captain, her sixth or seventh, Walter Paton, was engaged.

The first voyage of the season began on schedule, 7 May, but the passenger list comprising 31 cabin and 107 steerage passengers, could hardly be called encouraging, nor was the fact that the ship's stores had to be purchased on credit. The return trip, however, was a resounding success, with 173 cabin and 216 steerage passengers and as much freight as the depth of the bar at Sandy Hook would allow. Not only this, but the ship's time for the journey to Liverpool, 9 days 12 hours, was the fastest on record by 12 hours. It was a propitious occasion for the directors to ask the shareholders to take a second issue of debentures, amounting to £4,000, to supply working funds. There was a troublesome matter of a claim by a Mr Parry for payment of £6,889 owed him since 1860 (there is a suggestion that this was associated with wine supplies) and there were other liabilities, including mortgage debts which had to be met. These seemed but transient annoyances, however, especially when the July voyage was equally successful and uneventful, and a further three voyages were in prospect to take advantage of the increased traffic occasioned by the second Great Exhibition in London. A new, more prosperous chapter seemed to be opening for the *Great Eastern*; her jinx had been laid at last. There were, however, certain logistical facts which could not be ignored by the knowledgeable. The ship was just too large for the Atlantic trade of the time and her average speed of 13 to 14 knots was matched by her fastest competitors, such as the *Persia* (1856) and *Scotia* (1862) of the Cunard line, which were much smaller and therefore operated at full capacity. In addition, the new fast ships had the advantage of recent improvements in the efficiency of their power plant, that is, more power was produced by their engines per ton of coal burned.

Much was said about the *Great Eastern* being underpowered. She was indeed underpowered for the speed of 18 knots glibly bandied about while she was under construction, and doubtless her designers hoped for this speed. The prediction of the power required to achieve a given speed with a given hull was a very empirical matter and rather should it surprise us that Russell came so close to the 15 knots he used as his target. Let us not refer contemptuously to the faulty premises upon which his predictions were attempted. He was in advance of his predecessors and in possession of much of the truth. Naval architects only later learned to manipulate and interpret tank tests assisted by a better understanding of the hydrodynamics involved, yet even they were sometimes deceived. The fuel economy of the *Great Eastern* could have been enhanced by working her steam expansively, as Russell pointed out. That is, instead of the steam being admitted to a cylinder throughout the whole stroke of the piston, it was cut off, say, at one half of the stroke and allowed to expand over the remainder of the stroke. In this way more work was extracted from each pound of steam supplied; but the total work done was less than with full admission. Thus, although less steam was used and hence a better return obtained per pound of steam by 'expansive working', so also was the power of the engine to some extent reduced and hence also the speed. In the circumstances, on the Atlantic run, the *Great Eastern* had no speed to spare. The same restriction would not have applied on the long run to India. One must ask why she was not employed on the long voyages for which she had been intended. Was it, as W.S. Lindsay, the shipowner, suspected, that the Far East trade, or the mercantile practices of that trade, could not support her? No one connected with the ship seems ever to have commented on this. The evidence, of course, is very consistent with a conspiracy of the more influential directors to avoid placing the ship in competition with interests they may have had in other shipping lines serving the Far East. But it is just as likely that Lindsay was right. Perhaps indeed the North Atlantic trade seemed more likely to offer a quick return as

Captain John Vine Hall (*Illustrated London News*)

Captain Walter Paton

the prospectus had declared. This, originally, was not unconnected with the interests of some of the directors of the Grand Trunk Railway at one end and the Chester–Holyhead or London–Southampton railway at the other. The *Great Eastern* became not only a prey to speculation, but an isolated oddity, not part of a shipping line, not purposefully and competently managed, not supported by a mail contract—as were the Cunarders. In addition many potential travellers were afraid of her since she did seem accident prone.

Much was made of her propensity for rolling. It was unfortunate that she was, from all accounts, often in synchrony with the deep-beam sea waves encountered on the Atlantic. Her height out of the water would make this very noticeable on deck and the absence of sails or damping devices such as bilge keels would be felt, although the presence of the paddles would help a little. This gave a great impetus to the study of the rolling of ships, and despite the advances made in our analysis of the problem, it is salutary to remember that some of the great ships of modern times, such as the *Normandie, Queen Mary* and *Queen Elizabeth*, showed a disconcerting tendency to roll excessively on occasion—a tendency to which the modern answer has been retractable stablizing fins. It is a wonder that no one suggested the like for the *Great Eastern*, she prompted so many 'modern' ideas.

Despite her disadvantages, the *Great Eastern*, by the time of her third voyage of 1862 was offering some promise of at least being able to hold her own; but ill fortune had one more trick to play, exploiting her great size this time to disadvantage. She had made yet another comfortable crossing when she arrived off Montauk Point in the approaches to New York soon after midnight on 26 August. In the process of hoving-to, to take on the pilot, about two miles north-east of the lighthouse, she startled the captain and crew by lurching peculiarly once or twice then heeling over with the suggestion of a list. It was as though she had gone aground or had struck some submerged object, yet the chart gave no indication of any outcrop of rock or sand to disturb the clear expanse of sea. Within a minute or two the pilot came aboard and clarified the mystery by telling the officers that they had probably just touched an uncharted reef called the 'North-east Ripps' (thereafter called 'The Great Eastern Rock' and later removed), a reef upon which seas actually broke in heavy weather. With so much sea around, it seemed all too unfair. Was the ship holed? The reports from below were reassuring, she was not taking water; but her list told a tale of water in the double bottom of the port side. No other ship could have survived that class of injury with such impunity. Startlingly enough, this was the first voyage upon which all the inner hull manholes had been fitted.[8] But how was Captain Paton going to break the embarrassing news to his suffering directors? He clearly hoped to keep it quiet until he could determine the exact extent and nature of the damage; but the circumstances of some delay and unusual behaviour alerted that incomparable news hawk Gordon Bennett of the *New York Herald* to the hint of something amiss. He decided the time had come to give the *Great Eastern* a little attention again and most unwelcome it was.

A diver reported a fracture about 80ft long by as much as 4ft wide in places, on the rounded part of the bottom. There is no report that he noticed at this time any of several other but much smaller fractures. The ship's agents in New York called in Edward S. Renwick, an eminent consulting engineer, and he, with his brother Henry, a former steamboat inspector, called on Captain Paton. One was practically blind and the other had only one eye—not very prepossessing in the circumstances. They were sons of the well-known physicist, Professor James Renwick of Columbia University and brothers of the celebrated architect James Renwick, who counted among his works the Smithsonian Institution and St Patrick's Cathedral, New York; august associations indeed, but perhaps not more of a recommendation to Captain Paton, a Scot, than their contact with Robert Burns through their grandmother, Jean Jaffray, daughter of Burns' friend, the minister of Lochmaben. It was Jean's eyes, strangely enough, which inspired Burns to write the poem beginning:

> I gaed a waefu' gate yestreen,
>   A gate, I fear, I'll dearly rue;
> I gat my death frae twa sweet een,
>   Twa lovely een o' bonnie blue....

Nature apparently made up for this by abstracting something from the eyes of her grandsons.

Renwick produced a plan to envelope the region of the fracture with a wooden caisson shaped like a long boat, contoured at the gunwale to fit snugly to the hull, and with access tubes down which workmen and materials could be lowered after the enclosure was cleared of water. The caisson, or 'scow', would be held to the hull by chains wrapped round the ship. The prospect of a complete repair being effected in two weeks[9] persuaded Captain Paton to favour repairs rather than risk returning home with the ship in its damaged condition. The decision fell on him because it would have taken a month for him to have received instructions from England. To help him decide, the Renwicks declared that they would ask payment only if they were successful. In the event, iron plates of the requisite size were in short supply on account of the demands of the war and the labour involved in the task was much greater than had been anticipated, so that the repair took nearly three months to accomplish.

It was during some of the preliminary surveying that a diver reported with obvious terror that he had heard persistent tapping from inside the shell of the ship. He was sure this could only come from the ghost of an entombed riveter. It may be that this was the source of the rumour of the trapped rivet boy, but if not, it certainly gave the story further credence. Captain Paton soon discovered, however, that the cause of the tapping was merely the shackle of a cable intermittently striking the hull. But the macabre tale had a life as long as the ship and was revived with every hammering noise from the hull which could not immediately be explained.[10]

Despite the presence of some superstitious fears, Renwick managed to fit a wooden 'scow' 104ft long × 15ft wide × 8ft deep to the hull as planned. When the Brussels carpet material he used as a seal proved useless, he resorted to the ingenious expedient of hollowing out the edge of the scow to take a 2–3in water hose which, when the scow was held in place with chains, was pumped full of water to make a splendid watertight seal all along the contact surface. This was aided by the hydrostatic pressure on the outside of the scow when the water inside was pumped out. Access to the scow was at each end by way of 6ft square wooden shafts reaching almost to deck level and also by the manholes into the double bottom compartments affected. Oil lamps and candles illuminated the interior of the scow and despite such claustrophobic conditions with many superstitions and other anxieties of the platers and riveters, a good repair was made. Whatever is said by the layman about the *Great Eastern*, it remained for the engineer an inspiration, demanding always something extra from those who worked upon her.

Paton was misled and was wrong in deciding upon the repair,

made at a cost of about £70,000 and loss of the revenue which could have been gained by a prompt return home. The patch of the hull was not particularly watertight in any case and about eight other gashes were left untouched. Furthermore, repairs could have been effected more cheaply in England. Thus it befell that the season which promised to be the great ship's best, turned out, through this simple accident, to be another disappointment. She returned to Liverpool early in January with some compensation in the shape of a good cargo, and preparations were made to beach her on a gridiron at New Ferry on the Cheshire side of the Mersey where the tediously awkward procedure of excavating trenches below her with nothing but pick and shovel, was carried out. By this means it was found that there were indeed ten gashes in the outer skin of the hull. The damaged webs and hull plates were expensive to repair, but the Board of Trade would not permit their being ignored. Some boiler repairs were also necessary. Nevertheless, all was attended to in time for the unhappy ship to set out for New York again in May on the first of three voyages planned for the year, 1863. This was her most successful season, during which she conveyed more passengers than ever—about

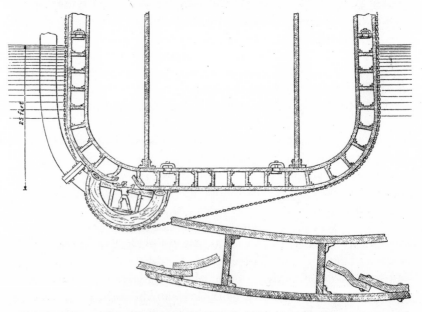

FIG 2 The wooden 'scow' fitted by the New York engineer Edward Renwick to enable repairs to be carried out after the hull was damaged on an uncharted reef in 1862

2,700 to New York and about 950 return, showing receipts of £37,308. The expenses, however, were a perplexing £20,000 in excess of this, and it must have been very depressing for the long-suffering shareholders when, despite the gains of the voyages, the directors had yet another gloomy report to make.

The costs arising from the accident at Montauk, uncushioned by insurance, had made a bad start for the year they said, and on the last trip out to New York the ship had run into a storm during which she had again fallen into the trough of the waves as on the infamous occasion of two years before, despite the efforts of twenty-three men lashed to the wheels during the night. Clearly this was a weakness. One of the paddle wheels was largely carried away and the remainder of the journey was completed by the screw. Again delayed for repairs, she returned in September only to cut down a small sailing ship *Jane* near the Irish coast with some loss of life and the prospect of further claims. The Cunard and Inman Lines had cut fares in their competition with one another and this had held down the fares on the *Great Eastern* to a level which resulted in £20,000 less revenue than would have accrued at 1862 rates; also, Mr Parry had accepted a second mortgage on the ship, for £5,350, as settlement of his claim. Taking everything into account the Company was in the red to the amount of about £18,979 and the directors had decided to throw in the towel. The total debts of the Company amounted to about £142,350 including mortgages; the subscriber capital was £403,404, the property a dead duck.

The creditors of the Company, including Captain Paton who had signed a bill for £3,000 at New York on behalf of the Company and for which he was liable, met in Liverpool to discuss the protection of their interests, having heard of a suggestion to auction off the ship. They preferred the novel idea of a lottery conducted from a continental centre such as Frankfurt-on-Main; lotteries being illegal in Britain.

At a contentious meeting of the Company—most of the meetings seem to have been contentious—William Hawes was appointed its official liquidator against the opposition of those who suspected his purpose, he having been in constant dispute with the use, or abuse, of the ship on the Atlantic instead of on the long voyage to India. It was believed that he was conniving with certain financiers to carry out his object.[11]

The creditors favouring a lottery presented their matured proposal to the liquidators at a meeting of the shareholders held at the Albion Hotel, Manchester, on 5 January 1864. The chairman observed that while the lottery as proposed would pay off the mortgagees, creditors and preference shareholders, it would not, as far as he could see, benefit the original shareholders; a commendable sensibility in the circumstances. Fortunately, the lottery operator, Mr Fabricus, was on hand to answer questions, along with Mr Stoess, the consul for Frankfurt at Liverpool, who testified to Mr Fabricus' credentials. The meeting was somewhat persuaded and formed a committee to pursue the matter, at least to the extent of asking the Court of Chancery to delay the enforced sale of the vessel for a few weeks. There was little prospect for the ordinary shareholders retrieving anything in any event.

All was in vain, however, and the ship was put up for auction two weeks later, at Liverpool, on 14 January 1864. The auctioneer, not inappropriately named Joseph Cunard, of Messrs Cunard, Wilson and Co, mounted his rostrum in the room customarily devoted to cotton sales, and called the assembled crowd to order. He optimistically urged all to make their bids promptly, an exhortation which seemed all too irrelevant when no one showed any willingness even to start the bidding at all. Undaunted, the auctioneer announced that he had been bid £50,000 and that a nod or a wink would be worth £1,000 and 'very cheap at the money'. A ripple of nervous laughter spread across the assembly, but further importunities from the auctioneer failed to elicit response and it became evident that most of the people present were motivated by curiosity rather than by any serious purpose. The auctioneer, with a sigh of disgust, announced that to save the time of the gentlemen present he would resort to the disagreeable expedient of putting in the owner's bid of £130,000, the amount necessary to pay off all judgement claims against the ship. But on no advance being made on this he withdrew the ship from sale.

Meantime, Cyrus Field, the mainspring of the Atlantic Cable Company, who had already promoted partially successful attempts to lay a cable across the Atlantic in the years 1855–7, had arrived in London to raise capital for another attempt with a better cable. He soon recruited Thomas Brassey and John Pender, MP, both enjoying fortunes acquired in different ways from the promotion, construction and operation of railways. Pender proposed as a first step the purchase and merger of the two companies involved in the design and manufacture of submarine telegraph cable—Glass, Elliot and Company and the London Gutta Percha Company—and with the co-operation of Mr Glass, this was rapidly effected. It is difficult to believe that the availability of the *Great Eastern* at this time was just a coincidence. The great ship had frequently been suggested as the ideal vehicle for laying a transatlantic cable. Brunel himself it seems first alluded to it in a conversation with Cyrus Field in 1857, and indeed the suggestion had again been made as recently as the Company meeting held to elect an official liquidator, to which we have just referred.

Some of the directors and shareholders were averse to the idea, however, on the grounds that it seemed unlikely to benefit them.[12] But there can be little doubt that Field and Brassey had set their eyes on the *Great Eastern* and events certainly played into their hands when the auction failed. The ship was then possessed by its bondholders, of whom Brassey was one, and Field and Brassey persuaded Gooch and Barber, also bondholders, to join them in buying out as many of the other bondholders as would give them control of the ship's disposal. In anticipation of being able to purchase the ship, they formed themselves into a company which they named The Great Eastern Steamship Company. This done, and it was all done very quickly, they put up the ship for auction again with the intention of buying her if she went for £80,000 or less.[13] Then, as Gooch blandly explained in his journal: 'Mr Barber went down to Liverpool to attend the sale when, strange to state, a ship that had cost a million of money and was worth £100,000 for the materials in her, was sold to us for £25,000.' They decently offered the other bondholders the option of joining the new company with shares to the value of their bonds, allowing those who did not wish to join their due proportions of the purchase price. The Great Eastern Co then chartered the ship to the Telegraph Construction Co, duly formed in April, for £50,000 of cable shares, all costs of adaptation of the ship for its new task and all expenses to be borne by the telegraph company. This may have come as a surprise to most, who expected the new Great Eastern Co to run the ship to India. She had a new rendezvous with destiny and her greatest role to play.

7
CABLE LAYING
AND CHARTERING

Now at last the two greatest engineering enterprises of the decade were drawn together. No other ship could carry all the cable nor provide so steady and manoeuvrable a platform from which to string it out along the ocean floor. There was ample room for the necessary machinery and monitoring instruments and accommodation for the crew and operators. The technological challenge was considerable, and although one cable had actually been laid, the brevity of its life—about 300 messages—suggested that its maintenance was an even more troublesome problem. It was widely suspected by the cautious that a cable at the bottom of the Atlantic was subject to natural forces or effects of unknown complexity. The commercial rewards were potentially immense. It was incidental to the promoters that the course of history could be influenced by the establishment of almost instantaneous communication across the Atlantic. Messages which, at best, now took nine days to travel, would be delivered in a few minutes. The Governments were interested, of course, but were sceptical since some shorter submarine cables had failed. They left the speculation to the entrepreneurs, and, in the case of the British, offered the prospect of a subsidy in the operation of the completed cable. The British Admiralty, however, lent two warships, the *Terror* and the *Sphinx*, to assist, and two hulks in which loads of cable could be hauled from Greenwich to the *Great Eastern* at her anchorage off Sheerness on the Thames.

There were now three companies interested in laying an Atlantic cable: the Atlantic Telegraph Co and the New York, Newfoundland and London Telegraph Co promoted by Cyrus Field, and the cable companies now merged into the Cable Manufacturing and Maintenance Co. In addition to these was the Great Eastern Steamship Co. Most of the capitalists involved had a stake in more than one of

Captain Robert Halpin

(*above*) The main deck looking towards the bow, taken while at Quebec in July 1861 (*Notman Archives, McCord Museum of McGill University*) (*below*) The main deck looking towards the bow from the canvas shelter in the stern while at Quebec in July 1861 (*Notman Archives, McCord Museum of McGill University*)

WHAT MAY BE EXPECTED AFTER THE GREAT EASTERN.

Presently the Ships will be of such length that their Bows will arrive at Port before their Sterns are in Sight.

By-and-by the Keels of such Vessels will have to be Curved to accommodate them to the form of the Earth.

Such a Ship would *force* a Northwest Passage.

What a powerful Engine of War it might be made!

As some part of such Ships would, wherever sunk, be above the surface of the Ocean, the old ones would be used to carry the Transatlantic Telegraph Wires.

Instead of going to the country, People would spend the Summer Months in a Rural Cottage on the Main Deck.

A proper regulation

(*above*) Cartoon from *Harper's Weekly* on the occasion of the first visit of the *Great Eastern* to New York in July 1860

(*below*) The scene in the dining saloon during the storm in September 1861, sketched by a passenger, C.F. Hayward (*Harper's Weekly*)

(*above*) The machinery for paying out the transatlantic telegraph cable (*Illustrated London News*) (*below*) Preparing to grapple for the broken cable (*Illustrated London News*)

the companies. The leading participants being Cyrus Field (both tele-graph companies); Thomas Brassey, Jr. (Cable Co and GtES Co); Daniel Gooch (Cable Co and GtES Co) and R.A. Glass (Cable Co). The Cable Co undertook to provide and lay the cable to the specifi-cation of the Atlantic Telegraph Co. Professor Thomson (Lord Kelvin), a director of the Cable Co and C.F. Varley, that Company's chief electrician, were appointed technical superintendents or arbi-ters. The chief engineer of the Cable Co was Samuel Canning and the captain of the ship was James Anderson, released from the Cunard Co. The Admiralty provided an expert navigator, Captain Moriarty. The Great Eastern Co provided the ship in return for a share in the cable revenue. This was all arranged between January and April 1864.

An improved cable was designed and by October a start was made to spinning out 2,300 miles of it, blemish free. It was coiled into the hulks in sections, then towed to the *Great Eastern*, where it was hauled aboard and carefully coiled again in three great water-filled tanks, themselves weighing 2,000 tons. These tanks, in the order in which the cable was to be payed out, occupied the after-hold, the forward-hold and a space hewn out amidships. The paying out machinery essentially comprised a row of pulleys to guide the cable out of the hold, and a large wheel round which the cable was wrapped twice before continuing through a series of upper and lower pulleys to the delivery wheel over the stern. Between the de-livery wheel and that preceding it ran an idler pulley constrained in a yoke to move vertically in proportion to the tension in the cable. This device, the dynamometer, was calibrated to indicate the actual value of the tension. An ingenious automatic braking arrangement could regulate this tension by releasing or engaging brakes on the upper row of pulleys. The cable was drawn through the mechanism by the drag of its catenary sagging to the ocean floor.

The mechanism for drawing in the cable was at the bow, since the ship could not be steered in reverse. If the cable had to be hauled aboard, it had to be grabbed and shackled to a wire hawser which was looped round the outside of the hull from the pick-up pulley and winch at the bow. When everything was ascertained to be secure, the cable had to be cut and dropped into the sea, then gently hauled in by the steam winch at the bow as the ship turned round to proceed bow first along the line of the submerged cable. The rate at which the cable could be raised was thus dependent upon the capacity of the winch and, of course, on the strength of the cable. The greater the depth, the greater the load, and another dynamometer was employed at the bow to indicate the tension, the maximum allowable being 7 tons. Drawing in the cable was thus a much more delicate and tedious operation than laying it, demanding very skilful handling of the ship.

By Friday 14 July 1865, everything was miraculously ready—all the cable, personnel and provisions aboard; all the apparatus assembled and tested. Next day, the *Great Eastern* left her native river once again, stopping at the Nore to take on a further 1,500 tons of coal and embark the last of her personnel. She now lay deep in the water under a dead load of about 21,000 tons. The anchor was raised by the same army of men pushing round the capstan, sixty on each of three decks, urged to their task by the sea shanty 'Slap bang, here we are again', led by a young fiddler perched on the hub. The old coexisted with the modern at every turn aboard this prodigious ship. She set out grandly on her new adventure with the eyes of the nation again watching carefully. Yet again she was the object of cheers, the vehicle of great aspirations, and the centre of attention wherever she touched on the outside world in her course down the Channel at a steady 6 knots. Her destination was Valencia on the south coast of Ireland, from whence the cable was to be unrolled to Hearts Content Bay, Newfoundland.

The scene on board offered further novelties, reminding one observer of an agricultural show, with its livestock—120 sheep, 10 oxen, 20 pigs, and scores of poultry—intermingling with blacksmiths' forges, anvils and carpenters' shops. The upper deck was kept clear for the cable laying gear and, being exactly one-eighth of a mile long, served as a useful uninterrupted walkway for such as Cyrus Field who liked to exercise before breakfast and dinner. When she had just cleared the Lizard on the Monday, she overtook a screw steamer labouring wearily. This was the *Caroline*, heavily laden with the shore end of the cable and struggling with the adverse weather. She was taken in tow. Gooch wrote:

It was an awful sight to see how she laboured and the seas washed over her. I sat up until past 12 at night in the bridge house, watching her lights. That on her mast head, as we saw it over our stern, was performing most extraordinary gambols; now it sunk down out of sight and again shot up into the sky like a rocket, and rolled from side to side in a fearful manner. It was difficult to believe that in the hull of that ship a number of human beings were living. We all felt very anxious for her fate; not only for the lives of those on board, but also for the safety of our shore end. Early the next morning the towing cable parted, but fortunately the weather had a good deal moderated. I will never forget those hours we watched the Caroline.[1]

Another, but less involved observer described it as 'like viewing a looming shipwreck from the comfortable boxes of a theatre'.[2]

All ended well, however, and the *Great Eastern* rested in Bantry Bay while the shore end of the cable was unloaded from the *Caroline* at Valencia and, supported on a line of small fishermen's boats serving as pontoons, was led up the cliffs to the telegraph station.

Where she lay in Bantry Bay, the *Great Eastern* was boarded by the locals who swarmed up the companion way from rude boats of all descriptions, and noisily jostled each other to be first on board, heedless of the danger of falling into the sea. They displayed all sorts of wares for sale—butter, cheese, buttermilk, salt fish, fishing lines, poultry, woollen stockings and the like—which the sailors purchased with abandon. One visitor stood 'inhaling the cherished odour', it was said, of the pigs and particularly admired the black species on board, one of which he fruitlessly pled with the purser to exchange for a huge white pig left in his boat below.

When the signal was received, the *Great Eastern* steamed off to pick up the end of the twenty-seven mile cable from shore and splice it to the great coil in the aft tank. This done, the flotilla took noisy farewell of its visitors and headed directly for Newfoundland, the slender cable slipping off the stern of the great ship at about 4 knots. A careful regimen of signals every ten or fifteen minutes to and from the shore through the whole length of cable, was followed, so that a fault could be quickly detected. It was for this duty that Professor Thomson had devised his mirror galvanometer, familiar to all students of physics today. The conditions were ideal and as the speed was increased to 6 knots and as hour after hour passed without hitch, expectations rose and apprehensions fled.

At about 4.20 next morning, however, the ship was roused by the booming of the gun and a halt to the steady motion. This was the signal for the escorts, the *Terror* and *Sphinx*, to close. A fault had developed in the cable at a point estimated to be about ten miles from the ship.

It was with many misgivings that the anxious onlookers watched the precious cable being cut then, precariously secured by a hawser, dropped into the water. The take-up gear lacked steam and, at about half a knot an hour, nearly a whole day was required just to draw in the necessary length of cable. At breakfast next day, it was announced that the fault had been reached at last. The offending section was cut out and, the necessary splicing accomplished, the ship, to everyone's relief, was turned again towards the west. But their joy was short-lived. Within half an hour, Canning again called a halt—the line was dead—and preparations were being made to repeat the tedious pick-up operation when transmission was restored; there had merely been some confusion with the testing procedure—what sighs of relief. Now everything went well again, so well indeed, that HMS *Sphinx* with the sounding apparatus was steadily left behind. There was understandable reluctance to retard such excellent progress after losing thirty-seven hours. It was known that the cable was by then being lowered to the floor of a valley nearly two miles below. After the previous difficulty, picking up the cable from that depth was to be dreaded.

Two or three days of steady progress relaxed all concerned, and at each test eyes were cast less anxiously upon the disc of light on the galvanometer scale. It was with something of a fright, therefore, that, with about 745 miles of cable payed out, the tell-tale disc flew off the scale, indicating a serious fault in the cable.

The tedious and risky process of cutting and picking up was conducted until the faulty portion was aboard and excised. This time there was a terrible knotting of the cable in the tank when paying out began again, but miraculously the chaos was unravelled and only nineteen hours were lost. The fault in the cable was discovered to have been due to a piece of wire driven through it in a way that suggested a deliberate act of sabotage. The tank crew on duty were suspect and relieved of their jobs. Someone among them, it was thought, must be the agent of rival interests. A system of surveillance was introduced and all continued without hitch for a further three days, by which time about 1,200 miles of cable had been run out. Newfoundland, but 600 miles off, now seemed within easy reach. Another two days and the continental shelf would reduce the depth to 500 fathoms. Then, on the morning of 2 August, Cyrus Field himself, watching the cable running from the tank, heard a grating noise and a workman exclaiming 'there goes a piece of wire'. It was overboard before the ship could be halted, but in that interval another piece of wire was seen projecting from the cable as it ran out of the tank. The testing room reported a minor fault and the usual retrieval steps were taken. Again the donkey engine driving the winch ran out of steam but, this time, during the delay, the wind changed and awkwardly drifted the ship over the cable, causing the cable to foul the hawse pipe on the port bow. The engines were gently reversed but the chafing of the cable was considerable and was blamed for its sudden parting at a point which was by then twenty-five feet on board. In an instant, the cable wriggled free through the stoppers into the sea and men gazed at each other, horrified and incredulous. The cable had gone! Was that the end? Canning thought so. A pall of gloom fell over the ship as the word passed round; there was now no heart for games or diversions and the piano was closed.

Despite deep pessimism, the cable being about two and a half miles down, it was decided to grapple for it. The ship was run a few miles from the position of the break to a situation from which it could drift across the cable. The grapnels, two five-pronged anchors with sharply curved and pointed flukes, were shackled to a long, wire rope and dropped overboard. It took nearly two hours for the grapnels to reach bottom with sufficient slack. But the conditions were excellent and the ship slowly drifted, dragging the grapnels along the great submerged valley floor. As dawn began to break, it was evident that a grapnel had entangled with something and when the dynamometer indicated an increase of tension as the rope was hauled in, it was clear that the cable had been hooked. It was too much to hope for, yet, there it was, the precious slender thread of wire and gutta-percha was being fished from the ooze and dark mystery of the deep, two and a half miles down. It was an awesome and exciting experience. Would the lifting tackle or the cable be strong enough?

The engineers watched the dynamometer reading slowly climb; then, when the cable was raised about three quarters of a mile, an iron coupling linking two lengths of hawser failed, and grapnel, rope, cable and all, fell back to the depths, taking the spirit of the expedition along with it. A buoy was lowered and a new grappling position was selected closer to the end of the cable to reduce the load. Another buoy was dropped to mark the new position and the ship lay-to since the wind was not blowing in the required direction. To settle it all, fog soon enveloped the scene. Nature had given them their chance and they had muffed it. Three days of waiting, drifting and seeking the marker buoy passed. Then, on 7 August, nature relented and removed the fog with a breeze in the right direction. Once again the cable was hooked by a new grapnel. This time, when it had been raised one mile another shackle of the line broke and another length of wire rope went with the cable, leaving a decided shortage of rope for another attempt. It was ominously apparent that the available tackle was of inadequate strength. Nevertheless, it was not easy to abandon hope as long as there was a grapnel and some rope left. Another attempt was made on the 10th, but this time the cable was not hooked at all. When the grapnel was drawn aboard it was found covered with a soft yellow pasty substance containing minute shells. Next day the cable was caught again and the slow process of hauling it in repeated. By now the steam winch had been forsaken for a manually operated capstan and a length of manilla rope had been required to extend the grappling line. When the cable had been raised about three-quarters of a mile, the rope failed at a splice, and the cable slipped into the unrelenting sea.

There was nothing for it now but to steam for home. There was insufficient rope for another grappling attempt and, in any case, there was no longer confidence in the strength of the equipment.

All this time the Valencia operators were left in suspense and people speculated (such being her uncanny reputation) that the *Great Eastern* had perhaps been lost in a storm. But reassurance was derived from the thought that the two warships were in attendance, which would have raised a wry smile on the faces of those who had watched the escorts plunge and rock while the great ship stood by serenely.

As the *Great Eastern* and her disappointed crew headed home, Cyrus Field retreated to his cabin and drafted the prospectus for another cable and cable-laying expedition. He was more optimistic than ever and, of course, there was cause to be. It had been shown that the cable could be raised and that it could easily be laid in operable conditions at great depths, provided the weather co-operated. The financial world, surprisingly enough, was not so sure. There had been too many scares, and it became painfully apparent that the capital for a new cable was not going to be easy to raise.

The *Great Eastern*, however, became the hero of the hour. The British public admired an heroic effort, a gallant failure which deserved by its conduct to be a success, and the great ship had suffered long. Admirably handled by Captain Anderson and revealed as eminently suitable for the historic task, her qualities and deportment were extolled on all sides. Her company was ready to offer her services (these being necessary for the prosperity of the directors' other interests) on the same terms as before; but the Atlantic Telegraph Co could not raise the necessary capital for another cable. Field took his problem to Gooch who proposed that they form yet another company for the purpose. The new company was called the Anglo-American and Gooch practically held a pistol to the heads of his fellow directors in the Construction Company to each take £10,000 of the new stock. In this way the financial snowball was started and the capital quickly accrued.

An improved cable was manufactured and the weaknesses of the lifting and laying apparatus aboard the ship eliminated. The procedure of the previous trip would be repeated except that three ships lent by the Admiralty would this time accompany the *Great Eastern*—the *Terrible*, *Medway* and *Albany*. Daniel Gooch did not want to go, but he felt his moderating presence was necessary on account of the jealousy growing between Captain Anderson and Samuel Canning, the engineer in charge of the operation.

The *Great Eastern* joined her cable to the shore end off Valencia, on Friday 13 July 1866, in heavy rain, and steamed off with her escort. This time the cable was laid with no serious hitches or any breakages, although there was one narrow escape when the coils in the tank fouled and came up in a regular knot. Only Captain Anderson's skilful handling on a wild, miserable night avoided overstraining of the cable while the knot was unravelled. Progress was awesomely steady, and when the *Great Eastern* emerged triumphantly from the fog, well into Hearts Content Bay on 27 July, she had completed the cable-laying in fourteen days. The rejoicing ashore was not a whit less than that on board. 'The joy', wrote Daniel Gooch, 'was almost painful; how impossible it is to give vent to such a feeling. A woman may shed tears of happiness, why should not a man yield to this also, as the only relief?' A message from the Queen to the President was transmitted, but unfortunately a little too early to be received at the shore station, the connection to land not yet having been completed.

The village on Hearts Content Bay comprised a modest collection of fishermen's huts or frame houses along the water's edge, surrounded by hills covered with struggling clumps of firs. The inhabitants responded to the occasion with jollification and, as seafarers accustomed to the intimate nuance of the sea upon their small wooden craft, they were especially appreciative of the wonder of the colossal hotel upon the water. They flocked from far and near, by fishing smack, sloop, schooner, horse-drawn cart and on foot. All were welcomed aboard; some even putting up for the night in sheltered corners of the deck.

Five ships laden with coal, which had arrived earlier from Cardiff, now began to unload into the great ship's bunkers. A sixth collier had foundered on the way. Also on hand were 600 miles of the cable of 1865 shipped from England in the *Medway*. This was coiled aboard and prepared for splicing to the broken end of the lost cable should it be recovered. Captain Moriarty, the expert navigator, steamed off in the *Albany* to mark the spot at which the cable had last been located. This he did with an accuracy which seamen thought impossible. When the *Great Eastern* steamed into view a few days later, having taken farewell of her good-natured visitors, she found the line of cable marked by buoys. When the conditions were favourable, she was placed to drift across this line with her three miles or so of grappling rope trailing. It took two or three attempts to hook the cable, each attempt taking many hours. Then, on 17 August, after long and patient hauling, the cable was raised to view. It was stained a muddy white where it had touched the sea bed and had the appearance of a spiralled snake. Alas, it could not take its own weight, of the order of fifteen to twenty tons, and relentlessly came apart before the eyes of everyone to fall back into the sea.

There were several disappointments afterwards and many frustrating days of dragging, waiting and hoping. So frustrating, indeed, that even Daniel Gooch began to lose heart, especially as the season was rapidly nearing an end. On the last day of August, new positions were taken up and the thirtieth attempt to hook and raise the cable was made. This time the cable was hooked and raised to within a thousand fathoms of the surface, then suspended from a buoy, while the *Medway* grappled further to the west and the *Great Eastern* took another bight between the two. This time the cable was hauled aboard in a great rush. No one dared cheer until it was decidedly secured and the signal to Ireland transmitted and returned to show that it was in usable condition. 'I think my heart ceased to beat during those few minutes', wrote Gooch, 'God only knows the sensation of such a moment.' The slender cable was threaded out slowly and carefully despite the storm which, had it occurred a few hours earlier, would have destroyed all hope of retrieving the cable that year.

The reception at Hearts Content beggared description. There

The *Great Eastern* picking up the cable of 1865 (*Illustrated London News*)

The *Great Eastern* off Brighton on her return home from the first attempt to lay the transatlantic cable in 1865 (*Illustrated London News*)

The *Great Eastern* probably taken in 1860–1 at New York (*Peabody Museum of Salem*)

Laid up on the Cheshire side of the Mersey at the end of the ship's career (*Peabody Museum of Salem*)

were now two telegraph cables spanning the Atlantic and joy and relief abounded. The emotional strain had been severe and it was with immense relief that the great ship, her travail ended, pointed for home without tarrying. Cyrus Field and Daniel Gooch were both wont to attribute their success to the benign intervention of Almighty God. For a time they were pleased to forget that they had planned to enjoy material profit from the enterprise. It was much nobler to serve as the benefactors of mankind. Her Majesty the Queen graciously bestowed knighthoods all round, adding ornament to the material speculations of wealthy men and to those who had done no more than their duty. It would have been rather fine if those who had created the *Great Eastern* and had fallen victim to her wiles, could have been remembered. Isambard Kingdom Brunel was dead and John Scott Russell was still struggling to survive her legacy of insolvency. A record dividend of 70 per cent was returned on the Great Eastern Steamship Company shares.[3] Times had changed.

The directors were ever on the lookout for an opportunity to charter their ship. There were no more oceanic submarine cables in the offing; consequently they were delighted to rent her out for £1,000 per month to a French company formed to engage her as a passenger ship to commute between New York and Brest in conjunction with the Paris Exhibition of 1867. The charterers agreed to install new screw boilers and to substantially outfit the ship at their own expense. This alone cost them £80,000, possibly more, leaving £20,000 in reserve. The *Great Eastern*, captained by Anderson, now Sir James, and supervised by the engineer of her Company, Brereton, was placed on a prepared gridiron on the foreshore of the estuary of the Mersey, on the Cheshire side near Birkenhead, to have the hairy grey weed and barnacles scraped from her hull. Over a thousand workmen swarmed over her, preparing berths and facilities for 3,000 passengers, and a section of the paddle engine crankshaft was reconditioned or replaced.

Her sailing date from Liverpool was advertised for 23 March, but she was detained for three days at the last on account of the difficulty of coaling in bad weather. The ubiquitous Cyrus Field and a prominent director, William Barber, were among the 123 passengers accommodated in Liverpool hotels until their ship was ready to embark them. Already on board, with the permission of Captain Anderson, was Jules Verne, the first of the masters of science fiction. He had booked for the round trip and was intent on experiencing at first hand the wonders of the first steamship which could indeed have sailed round the world in eighty days. On departure a pin broke in the mechanical coupling connecting the forward capstan to the donkey engine drive, thus causing the full tension of the port anchor chain to fall upon the twelve men manning the capstan bars. Unable to cope with the sudden load, the men were scattered right and left as the capstan spun back, violently ejecting the bars. One man was killed instantly and four were badly injured (according to *The Times*); Jules Verne reported that four men were killed.[4] The bystanders rushed forward to succour the wounded, the less severely hurt being taken to the ship's hospital and the others prepared to be taken ashore. The dead man and his seriously injured comrades were enveloped in sheets and lowered on to the deck of the tender which had been recalled; the whole tragic incident, casually reported one correspondent, detaining the ship only about twenty minutes. 'So lightly do Anglo-Saxons regard death', remarked Jules Verne.

The passage this time was an exceptionally long one—fourteen days—on account of some heavy weather and the need to 'run in' the renewed bearings. It is evident from Jules Verne's account (which is only partly fictitious) that there was still an aversion to fastening down tables and chairs. On one occasion he wrote:

I left my cabin, and helping myself with hands and feet through the billows of luggage, I crossed the saloon, scrambling up the stairs on my knees, like a Roman peasant devoutly climbing the steps of the 'Scala santa' of Pontius Pilate; and at last, reaching the deck, I hung on firmly to the nearest support. . . . Struck amidships by the waves, and with no sail to steady her, the *Great Eastern* rolled frightfully, her bare masts describing immense circles in the air. There was no pitching to speak of, but the rolling was dreadful, and it was impossible to stand upright. The officer on watch, clinging to the bridge, looked as if he were in a swing.

There were three or four distinct stormy interludes during the voyage, all of which presented their own particular excitement, including damage to the bulwarks and fatal injuries to one of the crew. When she headed into the foam-crested billows, the *Great Eastern* cut through them—as her bow was designed to do—but pitched somewhat more than was her custom. Captain Anderson was reluctant to run before the onslaught which Jules Verne thought unnecessarily stubborn of him. He described Anderson as 'a tall figure, with a broad smiling face, and merry eyes; walking with a quiet dignified step, his hands never in his pockets, always irreproachably gloved and elegantly dressed, and invariably with a little piece of his white handkerchief peeping out of the pocket of his blue, gold-laced overcoat.' He was a Scottish Sabbatarian typical of his time, insisting that his crew dress in full uniform on the Sunday, and refraining from requiring the sails to be hoisted, at least prior to and in the time of church service—'that which comes directly from God must be respected; the wind is in His hand, the steam is in the power of man.'

Unfortunately, the long passage had an adverse effect on the bookings and when, a week after her arrival, the ship left New York for Brest on the first of what were intended to be several remunerative voyages, 191 passengers rattled about in accommodation prepared for 3,000. The *New York Times* made an estimate of the expenses and revenue of the sailing and decided that the charterers were facing a deficit of around £80,000. This news would precede the ship by the telegraph she herself had laid. Her charterers took fright. In fear of being seized for debt, the ship stood off Brest when she arrived and no visitors were allowed on board. She disembarked her passengers by tender and hastily left for Liverpool where the crew were told that they would have to sue the French company for their wages. Many of the tradesmen recently employed upon the refitting also had not been paid and there were debts to the owners, in all amounting to about £21,000. The crew, led by its most articulate members, claimed compensation for the minimum of three months for which they had signed articles, and not merely for the one voyage with which the Company seemed ready to fob them off. The distinguished captain, Sir James Anderson, endured the indignity of having a summons made out against him for this liability at Liverpool Police Court. He explained that no settlement could be made until the exact liability was determined. Once this was resolved, he said, the Great Eastern Steamship Company would sue the delinquents. The crew, most of whom had mouths to feed and faced the necessity of engaging themselves to other ships, were in no condition to wait. Through their solicitors, they forwarded affidavits to the Court of Admiralty, as a result of which the *Great Eastern* was seized by the Receiver of Wrecks in security for the £4,500 claimed as wages. The Great Eastern Company contested this amount and agreed to a settlement in court to the amount of £1,500. The unfortunate wage earners could not argue for long. No dividend, decently enough, was proposed for 1867, the shareholders being reminded that they had done extraordinarily well last time.[5]

Despite the unfortunate collapse of one French company, there was talk of the formation of another to complete the engagement. This company, of course, would have been spared the expense of refitting which crippled its predecessor; but nothing came of this. Instead, the *Societé du Cable Transatlantique Français* was formed. This Company engaged the Telegraph Construction and Maintenance Co to lay a cable between Brest and Newfoundland in the summer of 1869. A prime mover in this enterprise was P.J. Reuter who was making great use of telegraphy in his rapidly developing news and intelligence agency. Although German by birth, he had been a naturalized British subject since 1851, the year in which he founded his business in London. Part of the service fee for the *Great Eastern* was, as usual, shares of the cable company, so it did not matter to Gooch and his fellow proprietors of the ship that the new cable would be in competition with the other cables in which they had a stake. Captain Anderson was appointed director-general of the French company and Halpin, his first mate on the *Great Eastern*, was appointed to succeed him as captain. Jules Verne described Halpin as: 'An active little man, with a very sunburnt skin, a black beard almost covering his face, and legs which defied every lurch of the vessel. A skilful, energetic seaman, he gave his orders in a clear, decided tone. . . .' The passenger accommodation so expensively restored was torn out to make room for the cable tanks and, heavily laden with her now familiar freight, the *Great Eastern* set out to connect up with the telegraph station at Brest and proceeded without delay on 21 July 1869, to lay her third cable across the Atlantic. There were the usual hitches, faults in the cable of that curious sort which suggested deliberate piercing by a wire, stormy weather and a maximum depth of over three miles to give concern. But the ship responded to every demand and rode the waves with her usual aplomb.

On her return to England she was loaded with another cable to lay across the Indian Ocean between Bombay and Suez. At last she set forth on the long voyage to India for which she had been intended; but under very different auspices than were ever imagined. She hooked up with the shore at Bombay around the end of January 1870 and successfully laid this, her fourth cable.

Thereafter, the illustrious ship was idle for nearly two years, riding at anchor in the Mersey and costing the Company about £70 a month. Then, in May 1873, she was used again to lay her fifth cable, her fourth across the Atlantic. The French Atlantic telegraph company had planned a new cable from Brest to Halifax but amalgamated with the Anglo-American Co, whereupon the termini were changed to Valencia and Hearts Content. It was now old hat to the veteran cable layers, electricians and physicists involved. They were enjoying a boom in the demand for their services. An unsuccessful attempt to locate the 1865 cable, which had developed a fault, was made on the return voyage. Then, in the summer of 1874, she headed out with another Atlantic cable made up of the unused remnants. This time, to reel it out in the contrary direction—Hearts Content to Valencia, perhaps because the ship was steadier laden.

Business was good, she was returning a dividend of about 10 to 15 per cent, despite the discovery that the secretary of the Company for fifteen years had forged certain dividend warrants to misappropriate about £30,000 and had also misappropriated £7,000 of the Company's shares in the British India Telegraph Co. The Company's bankers were sued for the money and the secretary lost his job. The matter dragged out for two or three years. The grand old vessel, now much loved by all who sailed in her and particularly by those who had shared the thrills and anxieties of her cable-laying expeditions, had, in fact, laid her last cable. By the time she had languished at Milford Haven for two years of further idleness, the prospects of her future employment began to grow dim.

8

THE LAST YEARS

It was going to be expensive to restore the *Great Eastern* yet again as a passenger ship, and, in any case, the great advances made in marine engineering had made her power plant obsolete. The hull, however, was in excellent condition and it was conceivable to install new engines and boilers of modern design, an expedient which it was estimated would cost only £67,000. Various proposals were made to the Company for her employment, such as fitting her out as a cattle boat to transport cattle from America; but none inspired confidence. Nevertheless, she was kept in repair by her own and the cable company and £2,000 was advanced to the Milford Dock Co to provide a graving dock to receive her. This does not suggest that expectations for the ship were declining; but the shareholders were becoming impatient and some urged strongly that the ship be modernized. There were many enquiries regarding her charter, but the terms could not have been acceptable, for nothing came of them. The directors were naturally loath to throw away their property and continued to offer the ship's use to the Government, but to no avail.

Soon the irresistible conviction grew that she be sold for whatever she could fetch. But when the Company advertised her for sale in September 1881, fixing £75,000 as her minimum price, the best offer received was only £30,000. In 1883, by which time the ship had been idle for ten years, Mr Barber, now acting chairman, informed the shareholders that attempts to sell or employ the ship had failed, and a few months later, the Company entered into a contract with a Mr de Mattos who paid a deposit for the option to purchase the ship for £50,000. This had some curious consequences; for soon we find Edward de Mattos alleging breach of contract and reclaiming his deposit, on the grounds that he had been refused the right to inspect the ship. The Company opposed this complaint and the matter went to litigation.

Meantime the Company engaged a firm of shipbrokers to obtain the best charter possible. Barber, and Marsden, a fellow director, joined with a commissioner of the forthcoming New Orleans Exhibition to make a bid for the charter. They planned to install the ship as a showboat at the exhibition, scheduled to open in December 1884, and were quickly fortified by the assurance of £3,000 from Messrs Mumm for the Champagne franchise and £1,000 from Schweppes for the mineral waters. Barber offered the brokers' agent a commission to recommend his offer of £500 per month for twelve months. But someone discovered the circumstances and, as a result, Barber was later incriminated with bribing the agent and conspiring to defraud.[1]

His son-in-law, with the curious name William King George, as a mortgagee of the ship, foreclosed, and the creditors took possession. This occurred in February 1885, and, as a result, the unhappy old ship was again placed on the auctioneer's block, this time by order of the High Court of Justice, on 28 October. A private offer of £20,000 was made by the liquidators, apparently on behalf of Louis S. Cohen, managing director of Lewis's emporium, Liverpool, one of the earliest of the chain department stores, but since acceptance of this was opposed by certain mortgagees, the Court disallowed it. At the Captains' Room of Lloyds, Royal Exchange, the bidding began with an insulting £10,000, accompanied by laughter, then rose hesitantly to £26,200, at which price the ship was knocked down to de Mattos who, a year before, had narrowly wriggled out of purchasing her for nearly twice that amount. The shareholders in settlement received only 12 shillings (60p) for each £20 share. De Mattos was director of a company called London Traders Ltd, which was reported to be planning to use the ship as a coal hulk at Gibralter after she had transported there a load of Welsh coal. The proposal met with difficulties and de Mattos chartered the ship to Lewis's who planned to set her up as a showboat and publicity stunt at Liverpool.

Louis Cohen engaged a skipper and a chief engineer to crew the ship and move her round to Liverpool under her own screw. Not surprisingly, there were many leaky joints and corroded fittings to repair on boilers and engine. George Beckwith, who had the distinction of having served on the *Great Eastern* throughout her career, was called from Swansea nearby, whence he had retired to a consulting engineering practice. With his help, the engines wheezed back into life and the *Great Eastern* moved slowly on her way, much to the relief of Mr Cohen and the 200 guests he had installed on board for the cruise. There was one delay as night fell, until iron mufflers were fashioned to wrap around one or two holes which had appeared in the main steam pipe. There was no peace for the engineers. Balloons were thrown overboard, each instructing its finder to write in to Lewis's, and painters were busy decorating and sign-writing. In large lettering on the port side was emblazoned: LADIES SHOULD VISIT LEWIS'S BON MARCHÉ CHURCH STREET, and on the starboard: LEWIS'S ARE THE FRIENDS OF THE PEOPLE. She was still the largest ship ever constructed, yet here she was, ignominiously creeping up the coast in garish array with a makeshift crew and a party of apprehensive socialites trying to enjoy the experience. This surely must be one of the first, if not *the* first, great advertising enterprises—another first for the great ship. She made a startling spectacle as she was escorted by five tugs up the Mersey to her old anchorage off New Ferry on the Cheshire side of the river. There she was stationed, out of the way of shipping, opposite Liverpool from whence in the weeks that followed, hundreds of visitors were brought out by tender and admitted to the ship at a shilling a head. She was still a great curiosity and, of course, a whole generation of young people had only heard of her among the lore passed down to them. There was a band to purvey music for dancing and entertainment and sacred music on Sundays. The latter, however, came under attack from the Working Men's Lord's Day Rest Association as wrongfully employing workers on Sunday.

By the end of July, there was a move by the proprietors to form a company, to be called the Great Eastern Exhibition and Entertainment Co Ltd, with capital of £100,000 in £1 shares. The first issue to be restricted to £60,000. It appears that the promoter of this scheme was a Mr Worsley who purchased the ship for £26,000. The ship was plenished with new facilities and appointments for her role of 'pleasure resort', and space was rented out to vendors and showmen for all the fun of the fair. The intention was to call at the larger ports of the kingdom on propitious occasions. She was towed to Dublin for the winter and returned to Liverpool in April 1887 where, moored in the Sloyne, she resumed her ignominious trade.

The main cable tank served as a music hall, seating 1,000 people, or as a dance hall, illuminated by electric light. Her several compartments and decks formed one great amusement arcade—souvenir stalls, coconut shies, shooting galleries, noise and bustle. On the decks were merry-go-rounds and steam organs in competition with a band in the stern. The crowning act, for a time, was the trapeze performance by a group of aerialists swinging between the second and third masts, scintillating in the limelight. It was the embarrassing fulfilment of W.S. Lindsay's recommendation of twenty-eight years earlier, an undignified end to an heroic engineering adventure.

Lancashire remains the great centre for fairground amusements in Britain, and it could be expected, therefore, that no port could surpass Liverpool for the great ship's new purpose, drawing upon the concentrated textile manufacturing centres of the surrounding country. Yet, even there, novelty seemed to have a finite life, and only declining business or the discomfiture of the port authorities surely could have persuaded the Company to move the ship to the Clyde before the summer was out. The refusal of a liquor licence by the magistrates undoubtedly helped. It was August when the ship dropped anchors off Greenock, the cynosure of all eyes; she had never before been seen on the Clyde. There she was served by the river steamers plying the great estuary, the object of numerous excursions from Glasgow and neighbouring towns, until the short, unsettled and chilly days of the northern winter closed in. The owners decided that it was now time to sell out and, in October, again put up the ship for auction in Liverpool. She remained forlornly at anchor on the Clyde, a prey to capricious speculation to the end. This time she was knocked down to the manager of the Company, a Mr Craik, for £21,000, a suspicious bid, probably planted on behalf of the owners, a fact which seems to be confirmed by the sale of the ship two months later to Messrs Bath and Co, metal brokers of Liverpool and London, for a much lower figure, £16,500. The prospects of the showboat trade could not have been so bright after all.

The ultimate fate of the *Great Eastern* seemed now sealed, but it was not until about the middle of the following August, in 1888, that her new owners placed a scratch crew on board and prepared her for her last voyage to Liverpool. Her boilers were steamed up and with the help of the steam tug *Stormcock* she moved slowly through the river traffic, out of the protective bosom of the beautiful hills and mountains of the Clyde estuary, hills and mountains which were to resound farewell to many giant ships in the years ahead.

The weather was fine, but the next day dawned upon dark masses of cloud. Winds, uncomfortably fresh, buffeted the grand old ship's hull, which, unloaded, was riding high, as she met the grey waves of the Irish Sea, waves which rushed towards her like old friends determined to impress her with their joy of reunion, and as determined to help her escape from her unworthy fate. They succeeded in their purpose off the Isle of Man, forcing the tug to cast loose and, when the great engines had to be stopped for a few hours, gave the old ship such a rolling that the funnels swayed and everything insecure was torn loose, including a large gangway. But the great engines had their pride, and when steam was fed to them again, they responded and held the ship into the wind, towards the Irish coast until the elements subsided during the night. With some reluctance, one imagines, the fettered giant was turned towards the Mersey, the tug casting another line aboard and leading the way. They reached the bar of the river in the evening of that day. Next day was a Saturday, and, as the *Great Eastern* proceeded up river, many thousands silently congregated at vantage points along the way to bid her farewell, most people finding it difficult to believe that there could be no better fate than the scrap yard for such a historic and magnificent iron hull. But alas, when she was grounded in familiar territory off New Ferry, it was indeed the end of the road for the great ship. Her fittings were sold by auction not long afterwards, to a great number of buyers who did her the honour of converging upon her from all corners of the UK and of the world. The receipts from five days of this amounted to £38,000, and artifacts and keepsakes of the greatest ship of the nineteenth century, the first of the superships, were scattered abroad, and it would be very surprising if many of them do not still exist, gaining in interest and value with the years.

The laborious and difficult destruction of the great hull began on 1 January 1889. Even in this the *Great Eastern* offered a challenge to technology, inspiring destructive ingenuity to the heights of the steel ball swung from a derrick, an appliance very familiar to demolishers today. It was a matter of crude brute force, endless battering, wedging, levering, sawing and chiselling before the day of the oxyacetylene burner. The public was curious, of course, to have the mystery of the entombed rivet boy solved once and for all. Captain David Duff, who had spent a lifetime in the Port of Liverpool navigation service and commanded one of the tugs which attended the *Great Eastern* on several occasions, told James Dugan (author of *The Great Iron Ship*) that the skeletons of two men were found 'inside the ship's shell and tank tops' and that when he heard the report he had hurried to New Ferry to see them. It is not clear whether he did in fact see the skeletons or was simply told about them, nor is the story thereby cleared of suspicion; it could have been another *Great Eastern* hoax, one, this time, which did not reach the columns of *The Times*. The story is too essential a part of the mystique of the great ship, however, to be summarily disposed of. That the double bottom of the hull had always been accessible, through innumerable manholes, for inspection and painting, and that some of the manholes were not closed until the ship had crossed the Atlantic a few times, are facts which only spoil the most durable of the macabre romances associated with the great ship.

Plate by plate, rivet by rivet, the *Great Eastern* melted away as though she had never been, and a further ten years were to elapse before the first ship to match her size, the second *Oceanic* of the White Star Line, was launched at Belfast in 1899. Although the *Oceanic* exceeded the *Great Eastern*'s length, she was short of her displacement by 6,000 tons. The new power plants produced much greater power with much less fuel and bulk, largely obtained from the use of higher steam pressures—about 200psi against 25psi—and the subdivision of the expansion of the steam into three or four stages in steam-jacketed cylinders. Advances in the understanding of the hydrodynamics of ships revealed that the lines of the *Great Eastern* would have been more correct if her speed had been 25 knots instead of 14 knots, and the new turbine-driven Cunarders of this speed *Lusitania* and *Mauritania* (1907), and the first ships to exceed the *Great Eastern*'s displacement, substantially illustrated this with their wave-line hulls.

The *Great Eastern* caught the imagination as no other large ship has ever done, or perhaps may ever do again. She epitomized the industrial and entrepreneurial spirit of her times and particularly the maritime spirit of Great Britain, but she was too big for the capabilities of her several owners, as well as too great a threat to the private interests of more than one of them. In the words of her builder, John Scott Russell, she 'fell into the management of amateur directors, among them men who had commanded ships, but not steamships; among them men who had made money by ships, but not by steamships; among them men who had built engines, but not marine engines.... The *Great Eastern*, the largest of all Brunel's conceptions, has read us all a lesson.'

Not long ago, as I stood looking at the model of the *Great Eastern*'s paddle engines in the Science Museum, London—the same

model presented to the museum by Russell over a century ago—I
shrunk myself in size until I stood looking up at the great cylinders,
wearily oscillating there above me, breathing steam and emitting
heavy sighs as the seven-foot cranks reached out, lubricators spark-
ling in the light, slowly turning the pounding paddles. The atmosphere was charged with the smell of hot oil and steam, the engineers
walked round, starry eyed with admiration and pride, rubbed their
hands on a cotton rag and checked this and that. The sensation of irresistible, inexorable, steadfast power, held me in its thrall. Here was
engineering's wonder and its beauty—everything about the *Great
Eastern* appeared to the people of her day in that light. Even now we
are still a little in awe of her.

APPENDICES

THE DESIGN AND STRUCTURAL DETAILS

The most significant original engineering feature of the *Great Eastern* was the concept of the double hull, essentially the application of the so-called cellular system of girder construction to the structure of a ship. In other respects the design of the hull, with its longitudinal and transverse bulkheads, longitudinal framing, and iron deck, was an extension of ideas already applied and pioneered by Brunel, Scott Russell and others with the help of Fairbairn's example and precepts derived from his investigations with Hodgkinson into the strength of riveted iron structures.

Russell was responsible for the lines and seagoing qualities of the hull and for its construction. His chief draftsmen, and shipyard

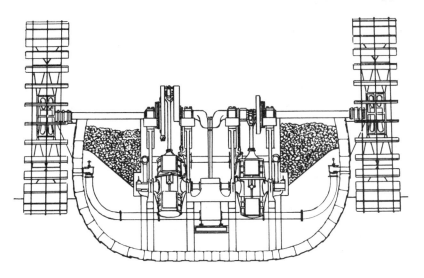

FIG 3   The cellular construction of the double hull, showing the paddle engines and the use of side tanks as bunkers

manager (Ned Hepworth), and charge hands, all played important parts. The engines were scaled-up versions of tried designs—oscillating cylinder, in the case of the paddle engines and horizontal direct acting, cross-head, in the case of the screw. The former were largely the responsibility of Russell's chief engine draftsman, John Dickson, and the latter of Mr Blake of the James Watt Company.

The construction of such a novel structure, of such immensity, with such expedition (ignoring the fateful stoppages) and such splendid workmanship, was a glorious triumph of the constructors. The Scott Russell Company of marine engineers and shipbuilders stood to gain immense credit and prestige from their great work had their financial fortunes been commensurate with their engineering skills. They put it to the touch and lost, and were not the last to lose by the great ship; but she has rewarded them with an honourable place in history.

The principal details of the *Great Eastern* are subscribed and it seems desirable to quote, as far as possible, John Scott Russell's own descriptions as being the most likely to convey to us the authentic spirit of the ship's designers[1].

The General Features of the Hull

John Scott Russell:

The lines are perfect wave lines (entrance, 330ft; run, 220ft): the middle-body, 120ft, is perfectly straight and parallel. The 120ft of middle-body give the ship roominess and ease in a seaway.... The vessel exhibits the points which I consider good in the midship section of a large ocean steamer; the widest part of the midship section is at 28ft draft. There is a dead flat on the floor, extending 36ft of the width of the ship, and the bilges are very nearly circular. From the water-line the sides tumble home gently to a diminished breadth of 76ft at the gunwale of the upper deck.

In the fore-body, the deck has much less flare-out above, than is generally supposed to be good for a sea vessel; but it is flare that is a main element in making a wet and uneasy seagoing vessel. By the narrow deck above, all undue weight is removed from the fine lines of the bow; and while there is a slight flare for the first 150ft of the bow, for 50ft more the side is nearly perpendicular, and the rest of the bow and middle-body tumble home aloft. Thus, there is a far closer approximation to equality between the buoyant power of the lines of the ship and the superincumbent weight of the hull, than if there had been a full broad flare-out at the bow. In this respect, as in many others, this ship is in remarkable contrast to the previous great Leviathan of her time, the *Great Britain*, in which flare-out and over-hang was carried to the extreme.... The tumble-home bow has my preference: the

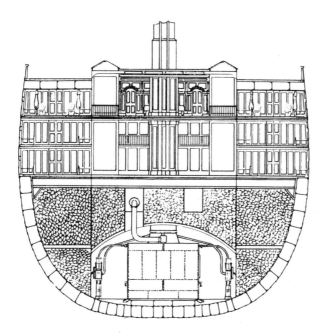

FIG 4 Section at the boiler rooms

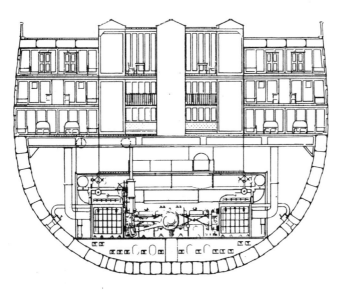

FIG 5 Section at the propeller engine room

flare-out is a concession made, as is usual, with most builders, to please the owners, but the amount is so small that it can scarcely be called more than a mere matter of taste.

In the after-body, the deck-lines, although full and roomy, and carrying their breadth a great way aft, have comparatively little over-hang, because the full lines of the after-wave body carry the breadth of the loadwater-line far aft . . . my own preference, also, is for a tumble-home at the stem, which, although it has long been resisted, has at last found favour in the Royal Navy; and will in the end, I think, be pretty generally adopted, in combination with wave buttock-lines, of which it becomes a natural adjunct. It is worth notice, also, that the stem gradually springs up from the line of the keel, which presents a gradually rising curve for about a hundred feet of its length. This gives the vessel handiness, and is also a great safeguard in manoeuvring in shallow water: for the same reason, in the execution of the ship herself, the last twelve feet of the keel turns up out of the way of danger, although it is not shown on the lines; so that the heel of the rudder is one foot above the bottom of the keel.

The triangular wedge-form predominates at the bow, and gradually changes to a sort of parabolic curve, ending in the midship body; and going on into the after-body. At the screen bulkhead, the section of the ship in the water is nearly semi-circular; and in the bulkhead beyond that, triangular.

The whole outer skin of the ship, from keel to gunwale, is composed of uniform strakes of equal plates, all of them three-quarters of an inch thick, in alternate outer and inner strakes. . . . All these plates are 10ft × 2.75ft × ¾in and weigh 145lb each.

The next notable characteristic is the complete adoption of the longitudinal system, the ship being built entirely without frames, on the principle (employed on certain of my earlier ships, c1850). This longitudinal system is carried throughout unbroken, without interruption by the bulkheads. The disposition of longitudinals is about 5ft apart, and they are 2ft 10in deep. They are placed on the centre of every alternate plate to the height of 36ft; above that, they are about 8ft apart, in order to form the water-ways of the deck; and on the bottom of the flat of the floor, in order to carry the weight of the ship when aground, they are twice as numerous and at nearly half the distance asunder, the rivets which secure them being all in the centre of the plates. These longitudinals are only half an inch thick, and the angle-irons are 4½ by 4½.

Another main feature of the ship is the longitudinal bulkheads, which run the whole length of the engines and boilers, and not only contribute materially to strength, but form bulkheads for the stores of fuel, which run the whole length of the engine and boiler space, supplying the coal close to the furnace mouth.

The next feature is the iron deck, also supported by longitudinals, the iron deck being composed of two layers of half-inch plates; the next characteristic feature being the introduction, by Mr Brunel, of the double bottom in her skin, and also the doubling of the upper deck—an addition which closely identifies the structure with the cellular-bridge system of Mr Robert

The paddle engine room (*Illustrated London News*)

James Watt & Co's screw engines (*Brunel University Library*)

One of the final indignities: serving as an advertisement for Lewis's at Liverpool in the summer of 1886 (*Peabody Museum of Salem*)

The *Great Eastern* under the hammer—the final auction of the fittings in December 1888 (*Peabody Museum of Salem*)

1. The Smith's Shop : A Relic of the Atlantic Cable, 1866
2. Auctioneering Under Difficulties : The Auctioneer at Sea
3. Spirited Bidding : Cigars Round at the end of the Day's Sale
4. Her Proverbial Ill-Luck Pursues her : Bidders Going on Board in a Gale

Stephenson, Mr Fairbairn, Mr Hodgkinson, and Mr Clark. . . . The double bottom of the *Great Eastern* extends throughout the whole of the bulky compartments of the ship.

In the ends of the ship, where the width is narrow, and the quantity of water that could be introduced in any given bulkhead is small, and where the bulkheads are as near each other as in the *Great Eastern*, it is absurd, and a useless waste of room, to carry out a double skin. Double skin, or closed cellular spaces, must be used with great caution and judgment, and should in no case supersede the simple subdivision of the internal room of the ship by numerous transverse bulkheads and longitudinal bulkheads. The cells should be large, and only used in large compartments of a ship [since access for painting and anti-corrosion maintenance is important]. . . .

The ship is entirely built with single riveting and double riveting being at the butts merely . . . the rivets are of a peculiar construction, giving great and unusual security . . . . The central bottom web comes in the place of a keel and with its top and bottom plates is ¼in thicker than the skin of the ship. . . . The whole skin and structure of this ship is formed of the simplest materials known in iron shipbuilding; two sizes of angle iron and two thicknesses of plate may be said to form the whole ship. To this, the exceptions are the keel, which is thicker; the stern and rudder post, and parts in their vicinity, and the round-up stem, all of which are vastly lighter, simpler, and less costly, than in many ships of far smaller size.

There were twenty ports on the lower deck, each 5ft square, to receive railway waggons. They were 5ft above the load water line. The bulwarks were 10ft high forward, and sloped down to 4ft 9in amidships.

Bulkheads

John Scott Russell:

The strengthening (of the bulkheads) is effected by vertical half-inch plates, connected by angle-iron with the bulkheads, at convenient distances apart. Ordinarily they run 5ft apart, but are shifted wherever convenient for the accommodation of the ship; and I call particular attention to the great strength which the longitudinal bulkheads and the transverse bulkheads give to each other; and also to the arch over the boiler-space, as well as to the longitudinal tunnel which communicates between all the engine-rooms, as all these parts are made to help one another.

The transverse bulkheads, therefore, divided the ship into eleven main compartments plus a bow compartment, eight of which were reliably watertight. The coal bunkers had a capacity of 12,000 tons.

Iron Deck

John Scott Russell:

The structure of the upper iron deck consists of long half-inch plates, united with inner and outer strakes, and double-riveted butt-plates, and in its general aspect is very much that of the top of a girder-bridge ... and it should be noticed, that every seemingly single layer of iron deck really consists of two thicknesses of half-inch plate: the plates themselves, being in pairs, break joint, and serve as butt-plates to one another; and it is only where they do not supply this function, that butt-plates are wanted. The butt-plates are projections, and the entire iron deck is covered with a carpet of wood plank for convenience and comfort.

Large spaces are left in the middle of the ship, to allow the central cabins to be raised two feet above the level of the iron deck; but between these spaces the iron deck is carried solid across, and the two ends of the iron deck are also thoroughly tied together. These cross connexions form a thorough joggle, to unite the two sides of the ship and the two sides of the iron deck thoroughly into one. The absence of movement and vibration in the structure shows that this union is complete.

The air-trunks, which descend from the top to the bottom of the ship, terminate in skylights at the top, except those to the boiler-rooms, which are uncovered. They contain ordinarily about 36 sq ft. The other openings seen along the centre of the ship are for masts, funnels, and skylights.

Longitudinal Section

John Scott Russell:

The general distribution of the interior of the *Great Eastern* is made apparent on the first glance at the longitudinal section. 350ft of the middle body of the ship are occupied by engines, boilers, and fuel, up to the load-water line; and the same section of the ship upwards is occupied by the passengers' accommodation, which in the centre of the ship is divided into two decks, and at the sides into three decks. This centre portion consists mainly of divisions, occupying 40ft lengths, or 60ft lengths of the vessel. Each group of boilers round the central funnel occupies a 40ft length. Around the boilers are the stores of fuel which feed them. The paddle-engines occupy

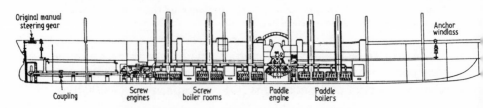

FIG 6

one 40ft space, and the screw-engines another 40ft: 10ft are reserved in front of the paddle-wheel engines for an auxiliary pumping and working engine. Here are the pumps, meant in case of accident to pump out the ship, and they are worked by two engines of 40 horse-power each. These pumps also assist to empty the double skin of its water-ballast; and provision was made there also, if necessary, to light the engine-rooms and the ship generally with gas. The same engines were, also, made to connect with driving-shafts to work the capstans of the ship. The communication between these different engine-rooms was kept up through a tunnel....

The Paddle Engines

John Scott Russell:

First it may be observed that these engines rest on four great beams, which run the whole length of the 40ft engine-room. These beams rise 14ft above the floor, and are, like the rest of the internal work of the engine-room, cellular bulkheads of half-inch plate and angle-iron. These beams are about 10ft apart, and divide the engine into three portions; viz a pair of oscillating-engines on the right, a pair of oscillating-engines on the left, and the air-pumps in the centre. It will be observed that each pair of oscillating-engines is coupled to a single crank-pin—an arrangement in favour of which I have

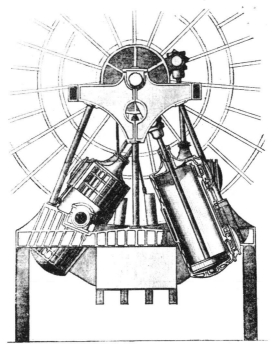

FIG 7 Side view of paddle engines

155

elsewhere avowed my strong partiality. The working of the engines is brought to the centre, and they are handled from a platform immediately above the air-pumps, which are worked by a crank in the intermediate shaft. The two cranks on the end of the intermediate shaft shall differ in no respect from the ordinary crank, and carry a crank-pin on which the two engines work. It may be noticed that there is no second crank to work the outer paddle-shafts; but, instead, there is a large wheel of cast-iron keyed on the outer shaft, embraced by a friction-strap, and into an eye of that friction-strap the outer end of the crank-pin works, and drives the wheels. This friction-strap allows the engine to be detached at will from either or both paddle-wheels, and was, I think, originally invented by Mr Humphreys; but I have added a peculiar arrangement of my own, which can be seen, on the model of these engines, in Kensington Museum, for enabling the engine itself to connect and disconnect these straps. But this also is a dangerous arrangement to be entrusted to unskilled hands, and therefore for the present has not been attached to these engines. . . .

The Screw Engines

John Scott Russell:

The screw engines are direct slide-guide engines, and work with single and double connecting-rod, each pair working one crank. The engines are thus perfectly balanced, and the condensers lie between each pair of engines on both sides, and adjacent to them, the air-pumps being placed in the condenser and worked by a rod from the cross-head of each engine. The engines are double piston-rod engines: all the pistons are attached direct to a crosshead, which not only serves as a journal to the connecting-rod, but also works the air-pump. The valves are worked by double eccentric and link motion, and the slide-valves are thrown to the outside of the engines, where they are conveniently accessible: these engines also are carried by a strong series of iron-plate box-beams, 6ft deep, athwartships. These engines were made by Messrs. James Watt and Co, and have proved themselves reliable engines, although at first sight one can hardly conceive that cylinders of so large a diameter and so short a stroke could cause a screw-shaft 2ft thick to revolve round a circle only 4ft in diameter, by cranks only 2ft long, which, nevertheless, they successfully accomplish. . . . A high-pressure steam-cylinder raises and lowers the link by which the engines are either sent ahead, stopped, or reversed.

PARTICULARS OF THE VESSEL

Length BP	680ft
Breadth (max)	83ft
Breadth over sponsons	120ft
Height (keel to deck)	58ft
Gross Tonnage	18,914 tons
Displacement	27,384 tons
Speed	14½ knots
Block Coefficient	0.57
Mid Area Coefficient	0.891
Floats	13 × 3ft
Number	30
Immersion, light	2ft 6in
Immersion, laden	16ft 6in
Slip of paddles	17.4
Weight of one paddle with floats	185 tons
Pitch of screw	44ft
Number of blades	4
Mean slip	17.9
Weight of screw-propeller	36 tons
iron in hull	6,250 tons
wood-work in hull	2,500 tons
paddle-engines	836 tons
screw-engines	500 tons

Engines	Paddle-Engines	Screw-Engines
Coal consumption per 24 hours	24123 tons	260 tons
Coal consumption per hour	5.12 tons	10.8 tons
Mean pressure of steam, lb/in^2	24	18.1
Coal consumption	11 lb/NHP	15.12 lb/NHP
Coal consumption	3.12lb/IHP	6.08 lb/IHP
Average speed of vessel	13 k/hr	13 k/hr
Average knots run by engines per hour	15.12	13

Engines	Paddle-Engines	Screw-Engines
NHP/sq ft of midship-section		
light	0.98	1.57
laden	0.45	0.72
IHP/sq ft of midship-section		
light	3.6	3.89
laden	1.67	1.81
NHP to 100 sq ft of wet surface		
light	2.17	3.46
laden	1.5	2.41
IHP to 100 sq ft of wet surface		
light	7.97	8.61
laden	5.53	5.98
Diameter of paddle-wheel and screw (ft)	56	24

NHP = Nominal Horse Power (an inaccurate measure)
IHP = Indicated Horse Power (actual horse power developed in the engine cylinders)

Boilers	Paddle	Screw
Number	4	6
Length	17ft	18ft 4¾in
Width	17ft 9in	17ft 6in
Height	13ft 9in	14ft
Furnaces	10	12
Tubes	800	840
Diameter	3ft	3ft
Thickness	12 WG	10 WG
Pressure	25lb	25lb
Shell thickness	⅜in	⁷⁄₁₆in
Bottom thickness	⁷⁄₁₆in	½in
Front plate	½in	½in
Back plate	⁹⁄₁₆in	⅝in
Weight	40 tons	55 tons
Weight water	40 tons	45 tons

The boilers were double-ended, box shaped, smoke-tube boilers, fired port and starboard. The tubes were of brass and there were five furnaces in each of the four paddle boilers forward and six in each of the six screw boilers aft. Both sets of boilers were cross connected, delivering to a main steam pipe of 3ft 9in diameter.

Superheaters were fitted to the screw boilers to dry the steam and prevent priming. Each superheater comprised a tube and shell heat exchanger, the flue gases passing through vertical tubes and the steam passing horizontally through the shell. A pair were installed at the root of each of the three screw boiler uptakes. Encircling each of the two paddle boiler uptakes were feed water jackets. These provided an annular space of 6in and extended 40ft upwards from the root of the boiler flue uptake. The feedwater could be directed through these to the boilers; the static head of the water in the heater being judged sufficient to feed the water into the boiler under normal operating conditions. To achieve sufficient static head to feed the boilers and to prevent a build-up of steam pressure in the heaters, a long standpipe was fitted to each. This extended high up the funnel then turned back upon itself down to the stokehold floor. A small half-inch hole was drilled in the bend at the top to eliminate syphoning. Not only did these heaters serve to retrieve heat which was otherwise going to waste but also to insulate the saloons through which the funnels passed.

The total boiler heating surface was 49,200sq ft with a total grate area of 2328sq ft. The bunkers were self-trimming and fed the coal right down to the stokehold floor opposite each furnace door, there being a 9ft alleyway between the bunkers and the furnace doors.

The flues discharged into a manifold running fore and aft on both sides of each battery of boilers and the uptake connections were located between each pair of boilers.

The feed was drawn from a sea water main which also supplied the bilge and ballast requirements. The feed pumps, one to each boiler, were driven by 10hp steam donkey engines, and were of the banjo type. Any one pump could supply any of the boilers. The designed working pressure was 30 psi but the operational pressure rarely exceeded 25 psi and was often as low as 18 psi.

The incrustation deposited by the sea water on the boiler tubes was certainly regarded as thermally undesirable and perhaps a source of overheating of the tubes, but it was also regarded as a barrier to corrosion. The saline sludge which collected at the bottom

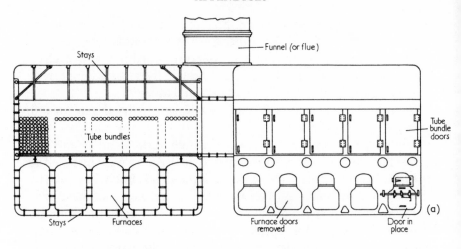

FIG 8 Fore and aft view of one pair of paddle boilers showing (left) the furnace front removed

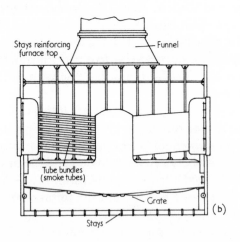

FIG 9 Cross-section through a paddle boiler

of the boilers was ejected periodically by blowing down. Fresh water was regarded as a corrosive medium and this was one reason for rejecting surface condensers. Another was the problem of the carry-over of tallow from the engine cylinders, these being at that time lubricated by tallow.

160

Condensers

The condensers were of the jet type, two for the paddle engine and four for the screw engine. Each condenser had its own air pump which could do duty as a circulating or extraction pump and even, if necessary, as a feed pump. The surface condenser was not favoured, for the reasons given above, and also since it was more expensive than the jet condenser.

The condenser injectors were supplied directly from the sea through a Kingston non-return shut-off valve on the ship's side and the amount of water injected into the condenser was regulated by means of a stopcock controlled from the manoeuvring platform—hence the term 'main injection'. Another cock on the condenser was fitted with a pipe and strum and led to the bilge, whereby the condenser and its air pump could be used as an emergency bilge pump—hence the term 'bilge injection'.

Auxiliaries

There were no electric generators nor was there steam or hot water heating (perhaps this was not considered so important as ventilation on the Australian run). Illumination by acetylene gas manufactured on board had been intended but only the engine rooms and part of the accommodation were served in this way. Otherwise lighting was by oil lamps and heating by centrally placed coal or coke stoves. A plan to illuminate the deck with electric arc lamps attached to the masts 'to diffuse a perpetual moonlight' was abandoned. The more difficult but more essential provision of power to windlasses fore and aft to assist in the raising of the anchors, handling of sails and like tasks, however, was attempted. Since the low pressure saturated steam available could not easily be conducted over the great distances to the bow and stern it was preferred to transmit the power by shafting from 40hp donkey engines installed in both the paddle and the screw engine rooms. These engines were also adapted to receive connections for working pumps. Most of the pumps, too, were multi-purpose, being available for bilge, ballast or fire duties. The donkey engine in the screw engine room was also used as a barring engine, the screw being kept turning slowly to relieve the strain on the anchor cables and also to reduce the drag when the ship was operating on paddle wheels only.

Propeller

The screw propeller was of cast iron, 24ft in diameter, and 37ft pitch, and weighed 36 tons. Fig 10 shows in the darkly shaded part, the solidity of the large castings which form the boss, which is cylindrical, and 8ft in diameter, and it also shows the set of each arm in the boss. In Scott Russell's words:

Each arm is held down by 12 bolts 2½in in diameter. It is to be observed that the structure of the boss is a hollow casting, entirely accessible from within, so that all the bolts can be made fast by nuts screwed from within, and countersunk on the outside. The general form of the boss is a portion of a sphere flattened at the fore end, where it fits the circular boss of the stern post, and the after part of the screw boss is closed by a thin wrought iron casing. The arms of the screw have been made smaller than they were at the time they were designed, but since then, much smaller arms have become generally used.

The section at the bottom left shows the manner in which the two sides of the boss are kept together. It also shows two large wrought-iron rings, which are fastened on both sides of the boss, and also two rings on each side

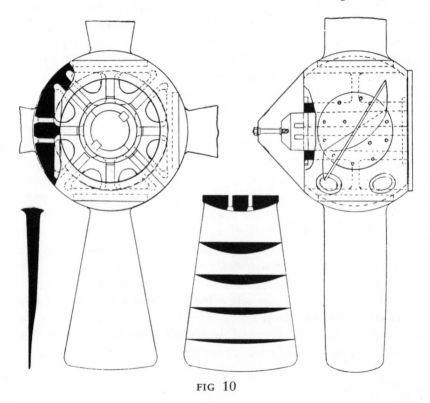

FIG 10

of the joint, also let into the boss of the screw, to aid the 28 bolts which fasten the sides together in preserving the integrity of the boss.

The shaft was 2ft in diameter and 160ft long, comprising four coupled shafts and a tail shaft 40ft long. There were two thrust blocks, one immediately abaft the engine and the other, consisting of multiple collars, was on the forward end of the tail shaft. This shaft passed through a bulkhead, via a stuffing box, into the tail shaft tunnel which was normally full of water. The tunnel could be pumped out by disconnecting the shaft and drawing the propeller boss up against a grummet, access being from above. The stern bearing underwent several modifications and the comments of Joshua Field who surveyed the bearing after its deterioration on the maiden voyage to New York are informative:

Went on board with Mr Penn [John Penn who invented the lignum vitae lined sternbush in 1854] to examine the engine with a view to ascertain and recommend any improvements to render the engines more perfect. At present the shaft width is 2ft diameter, is borne in stern, in a bearing 8ft long [Fig 11]. The four blocks are of wrought iron and are 8ft by 16in. These blocks were faced with soft metal about ½in thickness. The shaft with propeller on and overhanging is supposed to weigh on the bearing 54 tons. The soft metal has been pressed out into thin lamina which had got to the top of the shaft which they say has gone down about ½in.

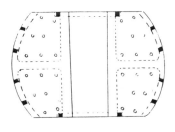

FIG 11

We could direct that the shaft should be covered or encased with gunmetal or brass, and that a gunmetal tube should be fixed in the stern, having wood fillets for the shaft to turn in. . . .

However, as neither of these alterations can be made without an entire reconstruction, we have considered that the present wrought-iron blocks which contain the white metal be planed away to the extent of 2in and a thick brass or gunmetal bearing fixed upon these slabs to have dovetail grooves cut in them, to receive slips of wood so that the bearing should be alternately brass and wood. This would be sufficient to do this to the bottom and two sides. The top might remain as it is. There is no wear on it. Such a bearing we consider will work so constructed for a considerable time and quite sufficient for a voyage to New York and back. The operation can be effected while the ship is afloat and in her present situation.

Steering

As built, the *Great Eastern* had only manual steering power through two steering wheels on the same axle which actuated a tiller by means of chain cables. Two further wheels were added, with provision for the addition of another four. We read of a dozen men or more being employed on the steering wheels in stormy conditions. The inadequacy of this led to the first application of power steering. This was designed by a very able and gifted steam engineer, John McFarlane Gray, then Engineer Surveyor to the Board of Trade, Belfast, whose contributions to thermal engineering science have belatedly seen some recognition in recent years. The new steam steering gear was installed in the *Great Eastern* in 1867 in time for her second transatlantic cable-laying voyage. The full details of this are to be found in the *Proc I Mech E*, 1867.

The designers of the *Great Eastern* were aware of the great forces which would be exerted upon the rudder and which would be required to move it. A note among Brunel's papers indicates that he contemplated the use of mechanical power to assist manual steering. There is no indication that he considered a balanced rudder such as had been installed in his *Great Britain* and in the *Adelaide*, the first of the two ships built by John Scott Russell in 1852, for the Australian Royal Mail Company of which Brunel was superintendent engineer. Trouble seems to have been experienced with these rudders or was blamed upon them and confidence consequently lost in them until E.J. Reed re-introduced them in the 1860s. Russell, of course, was averse to the employment of 'untried' ideas on the *Great Eastern*. He considered that the 'experiment of size' imposed sufficient challenge.

Paddles

The paddle wheels had radial wooden floats originally set at a diameter of 56ft with provision for reducing this (reefing) to 36ft, depending on the draft of the ship. There were thirty floats, 13ft by 3ft, to each wheel.

The Interior Appointments

The decorating and layout of the interior appointments of passenger ships present problems which are very different from those experienced in land-based structures. Ladders or companion-ways often take the place of staircases for instance, portholes of windows, and all the while there are exigencies imposed by the shape, confines and function of the ship—to float and move and survive in a very unstable, wet, corrosive environment. The decoration of the earliest sailing and steamships was the concern of the shipbuilding carpenters. Then, with the advent of the larger class of steamships, professional interior decorators were often also involved.

In the case of the *Great Eastern*, the decorators were Messrs Crace of Wigmore Street, London, who applied their taste and skill to all manner of living apartments at sea and on land. Indeed, it was Crace who designed the interior decoration of Brunel's earlier ship, the *Great Britain*, and most if not all of Russell's passenger ships. Not surprisingly, there was a tendency as passenger ships became larger to contrive their appointments after the model of the latest hotels and, indeed, to simulate conditions ashore, with imitation windows, gardens and the like. There was some of this in the *Great Eastern*, but in general, it was still strongly nautical in detail, still what we might call primitive but what her contemporaries might have called simply ship-like. Certainly one contemporary observer disparaged the Grand Saloon as an 'Italianate court' inappropriate to a ship. What he would have said of the saloons in the great twentieth-century 'ocean greyhounds', one can only imagine. A more recent authority on the subject has written that the equipment of the five saloons was:

completely adapted and subordinate to the ship's structure. On the other hand the materials used were of the most magnificent kind, and mirrors and gilding were found everywhere in great profusion. Nevertheless ... it will be seen that the decoration of the Grand Saloon, for instance, bears proper relation to the structural features, and might well stand as an example to many later shipbuilders and decorators. .... The ordinary staterooms of the *Great Eastern* were distinctly primitive, with six-berth cabins the rule. On the other hand, the 'Family Cabin', forerunner of our Cabin de Luxe, presented various well-thought out features, such as curtains arranged not only to screen off the sleepers, but to enable them to undress in privacy. The furniture, too, in these cabins was of more elegant pattern and in keeping with the best practice of the day ashore, while luxurious carpets were provided.

One other feature requires mentioning. It is generally accepted that in the 'sixties the White Star Line were the first to transfer their first-class passenger accommodation from aft to amidships, and the claim holds good so far as successful, regular ocean passenger ships are concerned. But in this matter, too, it was the *Great Eastern* which carried out the idea before it had been tried on any other ship.

Finally, she introduced a measure of separation between the third-class accommodation and the crew space, not until quite recently [c 1930] found in many ships.[2]

For details of the passenger accommodation of the *Great Eastern* one can hardly better the following contemporary account:

Running crosswise are twelve watertight bulkheads or walls, extending the entire height to the upper deck, with no openings below the lower deck: the ship is thus cut off into ten or more compartments, generally about 60ft long. . . . Five of the compartments near the centre of the ship form five complete hotels for passengers, each comprising upper and lower saloons, bedrooms, bar, offices, etc and each cut off from the others by the iron bulkheads. It is as if five hotels, each measuring about 80ft × 60, and 25ft high, were let down into an equal number of vast iron boxes. Verticle longitudinal walls separate each compartment into central saloons, and side cabins, or bedrooms, and decks separate the height into two such series of rooms.

The Chief Saloon is 62ft long by 36ft wide, and 12ft high, adjoining it is the ladies' cabin, 20ft long. The arrangements for ventilating and lighting the lower cabins from the skylight above necessitated the railing off of open space on each side of the saloon. Besides this, two of the enormous funnels find their way upwards through this room. These peculiarities all presented considerable difficulties to be overcome in the decoration. The open spaces on each side are treated as arcades, resting on light iron columns; and between these are ornamental balustrades, also of iron, of very delicate design. Both these were cast by the Coalbrookdale Iron Company, and are beautiful specimens of their work. This ironwork is all treated by a peculiar process in imitation of oxydised silver relieved with gilding.

Above, the columns appear to support, by means of brackets, the iron beams of the ship. There is no attempt at concealing these, but they are decorated alternately in blue and red, the under side being gilt. The spaces between these beams are divided into panels which are very lightly decorated in colour and gold.

The walls are hung with a rich pattern in raised gold and white, divided into panels by green stiles and pilasters in imitation of oxydised silver, to correspond with the columns.

The two large funnel-casings which occupy considerable space in the room, are octagon in plan. The four larger sides of these have been covered with mirrors, which continue the perspective of the saloon, and almost do away with the appearance of obstruction which before existed. On the four smaller sides, at the angles, are arabesque panels ornamented with children and emblems of the sea.

Mirrors are also placed on the large airshafts at the sides of the saloon, and on each side of them are other arabesque paintings with children personifying the arts and sciences connected with the building and navigation of the ship.

There are portières of rich crimson silk to all the doorways; and the carpet, of which the pattern is simple, the prevailing colour being maroon, assists in giving effect to the other decorations.

The sofas are covered with Utrecht velvet, and the buffets are of walnut wood richly carved, the tops being of a fine green marble.

A very peculiar feature in this unique saloon is the mode by which it is lighted and ventilated at the sides—by large openings railed off with gilt balustrades, and reaching to the upper deck, where they are met by skylights, which can be left up or down at pleasure. Besides the great additional light which these openings give, they are invaluable as securing at any moment currents of fresh air.... Next to this imperial saloon is another and still longer one, which is to be appropriated to the ordinary first-class passengers, the other being exclusively devoted to the extra first and the ladies. Around these two principal saloons the sleeping-berths of the passengers are skilfully arranged, the amount of accommodation being regulated, of course, by the price paid for the passage. But it is hardly fair to call them mere berths, seeing that they are, generally speaking, rather suites of apartments, comprising sleeping, sitting, and dressing rooms, all self-contained, and offering to females as complete seclusion as if they were in their own homes. The smallest of these berths is larger than the best cabins in any other vessel; and they have the peculiar advantage of being at least double the height, and possessing most ample and ready means of ventilation.

The cabins are not all arranged alike, but some are constructed as 'family cabins', and some in the usual 'two-and-two' fashion; whilst others, by a combination of both the above styles, can be turned into a suite of one large and two small ones, making up eight bedplaces altogether, all opening into each other, and capable of being shut out completely from the passage and the rest of the ship. Each family cabin measures 18ft by 7ft 6in, and is 7ft 6in high, and is furnished with every necessary convenience. The berths are so constructed that by a very simple process they can be made to collapse and fold together against the sides of the cabin, leaving a space of six inches between the two, so as to admit of stowing away the bedclothes; this done, curtains are drawn across, and so kept until night, the consequence being not only that the bed arrangements are entirely concealed all day, and the cabin turned into a snug little drawing-room, but that space is gained equal to about one-third of the whole area. The tables are so arranged as to be capable of extension or diminution in size. The cabins are floored with oilcloth, with Turkey rugs above. Under one of the settees is a bath, which can be easily supplied with hot fresh or salt water, by the aid of what are called the 'donkey-engines' or some of the multitudinous shaftings which are to work everything all over the ship.

The lower tier of saloons extend along the centre of the vessel immediately beneath and exactly corresponding to the first-class saloons, and form in truth the ground floor of the magnificent hotel, of which the others are the first, or perhaps it would be still more accurate to say that the lower saloons, with their flanking cabins, are the ground and first floors, the first-class saloons and their cabins thus becoming the second, for the superior height of the lower saloons enables two tiers of cabins to lie one above the other round them, short flights of stairs leading to the upper tier. It will be recollected that, in describing the principal saloon and passenger accommodation, we pointed out than an open space some six or seven feet wide was left on each side of the floors of the upper saloons, and was crossed by bridges leading to the cabins. The object of these spaces we stated to be the admission of light to the lower saloons. . . . The fittings of the lower saloons are of a far simpler and less magnificent character than those which adorn the upper, yet to our mind the toning down and subduing of light, combined with the great loftiness, produce an almost more pleasing and tranquillising effect. In the lower saloon, surrounded by all the substantials of comfort, and without any pomp and glitter ... one seems to feel even more at home. . . . The lower saloons, too, are the furthest from deck noises; and we much doubt whether between the tropics they will not prove the cooler, and, even if there were to arise in them a demand for more air, think what a breeze would pour down a windsail from the deck of a vessel tearing across the water at twenty miles an hour! The dimensions of these saloons correspond with those of the upper ones, the space on each side beneath that through which the light is admitted being occupied by a row of cabins with lean-to roofs constructed of hammered glass, which will admit plenty of light without permitting any curious first-class passenger to pry into the secrets of the cabins below by peeping over the balustrade above. The interior arrangements of the cabins are much on the same plan as those already described in those appropriated to the first-class passengers, only of course less luxurious and less smart, and accommodating on the whole more passengers. In fact, many of them, when their living contents are all berthed, for the night, will present very much the appearance of cupboards full of prostrate people laid round on the shelves.

The separate compartments into which the 'hotels' for the accommodation of passengers are divided are as distinct from each other as so many different houses; each will have its splendid saloons, its bed-rooms, or cabins, its kitchen, and its bar; and the passengers will no more be able to walk from the one to the other than the inhabitants of one house in Westbourne Terrace could communicate through the party-walls with their next-door neighbours. The only process by which visiting can be carried on will be by means of the upper deck or main thoroughfare of the ship. The saloons, together with the sleeping apartments, extending over 350ft, are located in the middle instead of extreme aft, according to the usual arrangement. The advantage of this disposition of the hotel department must be evident to all those who have been to sea and know the advantage of a snug berth as near as possible to the centre of the ship, where its transverse and longitudinal axles meet, and where, of course, there is no motion at all. The passengers are placed immediately above the boilers and engines; but the latter are completely shut off from the living freight by a strongly arched roof of iron, above which, and below the lowest iron deck, the coals are stowed, and prevents all sound and vibration from penetrating to the inhabitants in the upper stories.

There are two large holds, to be devoted exclusively to cargo, one at each end of the cabins. They are both 60ft long, and are the whole depth and breadth of the ship; each is capable of holding about 1,000 tons of cargo. The total quantity of space appropriated to cargo will be regulated entirely by circumstances. It would be quite easy to stow 6,000 tons in the hold and various other unappropriated places. The crew and officers are berthed forward. The captain has a splendid suite of rooms on deck, within easy distance of the paddle-boxes.[3]

Rigging

The rigging and masting of the ship were, according to Scott Russell, arranged to suit the views of Captain Harrison. There were six masts. The second and third were square rigged and the first, fourth, fifth and sixth were fore and aft rigged. The fourth mast was capable also of carrying square sails. It seems to have been intended that all the masts would be fabricated from iron plate except the furthest aft. This was to be of wood so that a compass could be mounted at or upon it. In the event, however, it appears from Scott Russell's account that the three central masts were of wood and the others of iron. The total area of her sails was 6,500sq yd, about the usual proportion of sail area per foot area of way; but very much less than she could carry if she were converted entirely to sail. The masts varied in height from 130 to 170ft from the keel to the truck. The maximum diameter of masts 1, 5 and 6 was 2.75ft and of masts 2, 3 and 4, 3.5 ft. Each mast was encased in a square tube of iron plate from keel to upper deck. In case of necessity, it was originally intended to make provision for the speedy cutting away of the masts by means of a crushing device operated through a powerful screw, about 3ft above deck. But whether this was really effected is not known. It was probably only of use where the masts were of wood. The stays were of 7½in wire rope except in the vicinity of the compass, where they were of hemp.

Construction Procedure

Upwards of 1,400 piles were driven to support the ship on the stocks, the Isle of Dogs consisting of a 30ft layer of mud, lying on a bed of gravel. The keel plate was then laid on a level platform of timber balks prepared for it. To this was riveted, through angle bars, the centre web; then a row of horizontal plates was laid along the top of the centre web and riveted likewise. Tall poles, or derricks, were erected either side of the ship at the positions of the transverse bulkheads. From these the requisite scaffolding was slung. The bulkheads and supporting longitudinal girders were assembled and riveted in place. The plates were all pre-cut, shaped and punched to fit in their specific places. At the same time the longitudinal bulkheads, and partial bulkheads, were assembled plate by plate and fastened together. The skin of the ship was first riveted at the upper levels, where it was not of cellular construction, then the longitudinal girders or frames required to support the inner skin of the double hull below the main deck level were installed. Then followed the riveting of the inner skin, then the webs separating it from the outer skin. The decks were fabricated at the earliest stage possible in order to provide shelter for the workmen as well as structural strength. The ends of the vessel were completed last, the stern being well reinforced to cope with the vibration of the screw. The engines were constructed—cast, turned and fitted—and assembled in their respective engine shops. In the case of the paddle engines this was accomplished in twelve months. Then the engines were dismantled and re-assembled in the ship. A wooden gantry was mounted on the main deck to lift the heavy boiler and machinery parts, access being provided by several large deck openings. There was a total of about three million rivets in the finished hull and each rivet squad of two men and two boys could install 400 rivets per day.

NOTES

1 The Conception of the Great Eastern

1 Ewan Corlett, *The Iron Ship*, Moonraker Press, 1975
2 Brunel Collection, Bristol, p 16
3 The first Court of Directors comprised: H.T. Hope (Chairman); G.T. Braine (Deputy Chairman); F.H.F. Berkeley, MP; C.R.M. Talbot, MP; J.S.G. Burke; R.J.R. Campbell; P.W.S. Miles; S. Baker; T. Bayley; E.L. Betts; R. McCalmont; Albert Robinson; J.E. Stephens; and C. Geach, MP
4 David R. MacGregor, 'Tendering and Contract Procedure in Merchant Shipyards in the Middle of the Nineteenth Century', *The Mariner's Mirror,* vol 48, no. 4, November 1962, p254
5 Report to Proprietors, 16 January 1856, *Gt. Ship Launching,* Brunel Collection, Bristol, p280.
6 ESN Co Calculation Book, p3
7 Directors' Report, February 1855
8 Quoted, L.T.C. Rolt, *I.K. Brunel,* Longman, 1957, p253
9 Letter, I. Brunel–Manby, 24 May 1867, ICE
10 J.S.R. to ESN Co, 28 August 1856, Hollingworth Coll
11 ESN Co Calculation Book, 8 July 1855

2 The Launch

1 *The Builder*, December 1867

3 The Fitting Out

1 W.S. Lindsay. *The History of Merchant Shipping*, London, 1876, vol IV, p358
2 'Eastern Steam', 25 February 1854, *Gt. Ship*, Brunel Collection, Bristol, p16
3 The correspondent could not have been Dickens himself if George Augustus Sala is correct when he writes in his autobiography that he travelled down to join the ship at Erith in the company of Charles Dickens 'who was on his way to his house at Gad's Hill'
4 *New York Times*, 1 October 1859, p1
5 *Household Words*

6   George Augustus Sala wrote in his autobiography:

> this I remember well ... I speak of the ministrations, equally tender and heroic, of the Marquis of Stafford to these scalded miserables. A happy thought occurred to him of how their dreadful anguish might at least be alleviated.
>
> It was to encase the bodies of the wounded in sheets of cotton-wool soaked in oil. There was plenty of oil on board, but alas! cotton wool was not ... Suddenly Lord Stafford exclaimed, 'By jove! there must be wool in those curtains.' In an instant a hundred hands were dragging down and ripping asunder the sumptuous damask curtains of the saloon and the side cabins; and these curtains were found to be lined with wool, scores of yards of which were at once at the disposal of those who were tending the wounded.
>
> *Life of George Augustus Sala*, pp347–8

4 Breaking Free

1   The committee: Rev Mr Nicholson, J.R. Croskey, Goetz, Taylor, Hope, Baker, Hodgson

2   These were: Miss Herburt, Mr and Mrs Gooch, Mr and Mrs Stainthorp, General Watkins, Lt Col Harrison, Capt Morris RN, Capt McKennan RN, Major Balfour, Capt Drummond, Capt Carnegie RN, Rev Mr Southey, A. Woods (*The Times*), J.S. Oakford (London Agent, Vanderbilt Line), Mr Murphy (New York pilot), Norman S. Russell, Zerah Colburn, A.L. Holley (*New York Times*), H.M. Wells, Mr McKenzie, G.S. Roebuck, Mr Skinner, D. Kennedy, G.E.M. Taylor, G.D. Brooks, Mr Taylor, T. Harnley, H. Marin, Mr Cave, A. Zuravelloff, Mr Merrifield, Mr Field, Mr Barber, R. Marson, G. Hawkins, H. Cantan, W.T. Stimpson, Mr Beresford, Mr Hubbard, George Wilkes

3   The official report of the Great Eastern's maiden voyage to New York:

June	18,	lat.	49°27',	lon.	8°45';	run	since	yesterday,	285	miles
„	19,	„	48°41',	„	16°12'	„	„	„	296	„
„	20,	„	47°40',	„	27°54'	„	„	„	276	„
„	21,	„	46°16',	„	30°03'	„	„	„	304	„
„	22,	„	44°50',	„	56°22'	„	„	„	280	„
„	23,	„	42°50',	„	42°40'	„	„	„	302	„
„	24,	„	41°01',	„	48°52'	„	„	„	299	„
„	25,	„	40°58',	„	56°10'	„	„	„	325	„
„	26,	„	40°58',	„	63°41'	„	„	„	333	„
„	27,	„	40°13',	„	68°56'	„	„	„	254	„
„	28,	„	40°28',	„	74°00'	„	„	„	234	„
	Total	.	.	.	.	.	.	.	3,188	

2,877 tons of coal consumed.

5 The Embarrassed Debutante

1   Pamphlet: *Letters and Documents on the Subject of Direct Communication between the Virginia Capes and Europe*, pp104–144
2   28 July 1860, p155
3   *New York Times*, 2 August 1860
4   *Harper's Weekly*, 11 August 1860

6 The Struggle for Existence

1 *Steam Shipping Chronicle,* 12 October 1860
2 *The Times,* 18 January 1860
3 Letter, W.H. Gibbs, *History Today,* January 1976, p59
4 *Ibid,* p57
5 *Scientific American,* 21 September 1861, p263
6 *Scientific American,* 12 October 1861, p231
  Steam Shipping Chronicle, 11 and 18 October 1861
7 *Scientific American,* 5 April 1862, p218
8 Letter, Henry Brunel–W. Froude, Bristol Coll, 24 January 1863
9 *The Times,* 12 September 1862, p 7
10 *Scientific American,* 4 October, 13 and 27 December 1862
11 *The Times,* 18 December 1863, p7
12 Letter, Henry Brunel–I. Brunel, Bristol Coll, 17 November 1863
13 Sir Daniel Gooch, *Memoirs and Diary* (ed R.B. Wilson), David & Charles, 1972, p92

7 Cable Laying and Chartering

1 Sir Daniel Gooch, *Memoirs and Diary* (ed R.B. Wilson), David & Charles, 1972, p 98
2 Dudley, *Blackwoods Magazine,* 1865, p499
3 *The Times,* 10 February 1868
4 Jules Verne, *A Floating City,* London, 1958
5 *The Times,* various entries 1867 and 1868

8 The Last Years

1 *The Times,* 2 March 1887, p12

Appendix

1 John Scott Russell, *The Modern System of Naval Architecture,* London, 1865
2 John de la Valetta, *The Fitment and Decoration of Ships,* Proc. R.S.A. Vol LXXIV, May 1936, pp712–3
3 *Pictorial History of the Great Eastern,* London, 1860

ACKNOWLEDGEMENTS

I am happy to acknowledge a considerable debt of gratitude to the following:

The library of the University of Bristol, for access to the Brunel Collection.

The descendants of I.K. Brunel who made their great ancestor's records available.

My friend the late John Hollingworth, M.I.C.E., C.Eng., for his hospitality and for access to his unique collection of Brunel and Russell letters.

The officers and staff of the libraries of The University of Western Ontario, and The University of Strathclyde.

Also the British Library, the Science Museum, the National Maritime Museum and the New York Public Library.

The Accident Research team at The University of Western Ontario under Leonard Thomas, P.Eng. for photographic facilities.

Miss Elizabeth Milliken, for her indispensable typing and secretarial assistance.

BIBLIOGRAPHY

Ainsley, T.L. *Engineers Manual of the Local Marine Board*, 1865

Bourne, J. *The Steam Engine*, London, 1876

Brunel, Isambard. *The Life of Isambard Kingdom Brunel*, London, 1870

Emmerson, George S. *John Scott Russell*, J. Murray, 1977

Field, Henry. *The Story of the Atlantic Telegraph*, New York, 1893

Fuller, R.G. 'The Great Eastern', *Student Transactions*, 1 Mar Eng, no 1, January 1962

Lindsay, W.S. *History of Merchant Shipping and Ancient Commerce*, London, 1876

Russell, John Scott. *The Modern System of Naval Architecture*, London, 1865

Russell, W.H. *The Atlantic Telegraph (1865)*, London, 1865

Smith, Willoughby. *The Rise and Extension of Submarine Telegraphy*, London, 1891

Verne, Jules. *A Floating City*, London, 1958

The Great Eastern Steamship, H.G. Clarke & Co, London, 1867

Newspapers and Journals

The Times, London
The New York Times
The New York Herald
The Glasgow Herald
The Illustrated London News
The Graphic
The Mariner's Mirror
Harper's Weekly
Proceedings or Transactions of:
   The Institution of Civil Engineers
   The Royal Institution of Naval Architects
   The Institution of Mechanical Engineers

GENERAL INDEX

INDEX OF PERSONS

SHIPS NAMED